GRADE
5

Differentiation and Intervention Guide

Parrot Fire Kris Northern

"Rather than zoom into the fractal you can zoom into the edge of it and continually find the same pattern repeating itself much like the shoreline of a lake viewed from a plane."– **Kris Northern**

Investigations
IN NUMBER, DATA, AND SPACE®

Power Polygons™ is a trademark of ETA/Cuisenaire®.

Use of the trademark or company name implies no relationship, sponsorship, endorsement, sale, or promotion on the part of Pearson Education, Inc., or its affiliates.

PEARSON

Glenview, Illinois • Boston, Massachusetts
Chandler, Arizona • Upper Saddle River, New Jersey

The Investigations curriculum was developed by TERC, Cambridge, MA.

T E R C

This material is based on work supported by the National Science Foundation ("NSF") under Grant No.ESI-0095450. Any opinions, findings, and conclusions or recommendations expressed in this material are those of the author(s) and do not necessarily reflect the views of the National Science Foundation.

ISBN-13: 978-0-328-62342-6

ISBN-10: 0-328-62342-3

Contents

About This Guide

Overview

The *Differentiation and Intervention Guide* is a flexible and versatile component that supplements the *Investigations* curriculum units. An Intervention, Practice, and Extension activity is provided for every Investigation. The differentiation activities presented in this guide can be used anytime after the session referenced, such as during Math Workshops, or outside of math time. In addition, a Quiz is available to use as a formative assessment after an Investigation is completed.

Teachers may also assign multiple activities for an Investigation to a single student. For example, after a student completes the Practice activity, it may be appropriate for that student to work on the Extension activity. Similarly, Practice and Extension activities can also be used to reinforce and extend Intervention suggestions, either during the Investigation or later in the unit.

Within each curriculum unit, a feature titled "Differentiation: Supporting the Range of Learners" appears regularly. This feature offers ideas for Intervention, Extension, and ELL related to the content of that session. The *Differentiation and Intervention Guide* expands many of these existing Intervention and Extension suggestions by providing teaching suggestions and/or student masters. The *Differentiation and Intervention Guide* also provides additional Practice activities for all students.

Curriculum Unit 1, p. 22

Differentiation suggestions are embedded in the curriculum units.

Curriculum Unit 1, p. 39

The *Differentiation and Intervention Guide enhances the existing differentiation suggestions in the curriculum units.*

Understanding This Guide

The *Differentiation and Intervention Guide* contains support pages for every Investigation in the curriculum units. The first page provides teachers with an overview of the key mathematics in the Investigation and descriptions of student performance. The remaining three pages provide easy-to-use activities based on the Math Focus Points in the Investigation. Each activity features built-in ELL support and resource masters for students.

Unit 1

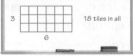

Differentiation in Investigation 1

Mathematics in This Investigation
The mathematics focuses on using rectangular arrays to deepen understandings of factors, multiples, and other properties of numbers (even, odd, prime, composite, square). There is also a focus on multiplying three or more whole numbers for a given product (e.g., 18 = 2 × 3 × 3).

Additional Resource: *Helping All Students Learn Multiplication Combinations*, pages 80–82 (See *Implementing Investigations in Grade 5*)

Understanding the Mathematics
Students easily build arrays and find all the factors of a given number. They are organized as they list factors and easily explain how they know they have found them all. They identify factors and multiples of numbers, know properties of numbers such as prime or square, and are able to use this information to solve the number puzzles. Students find many, or all, different ways to multiply three or more whole numbers for a given product. If given 18, students realize they can use 9 × 2 to create 3 × 3 × 2. Students reason about multiplication expressions they've found for one number to find expressions for a number 10 times larger (e.g., 180 = 3 × 3 × 2 × 10).

Option: Assign the Extension activity.

Partially Understanding the Mathematics
Students build arrays, and understand what factors are, but are unable to find all the factors of given numbers. They are less organized—perhaps only listing one of the factors (e.g., if finding the factors of 42 they list 2, but not 21). They are unable to explain how they know they have found all the factors or offer only a partial explanation. When solving number puzzles, students are likely to know what square and prime numbers are, but are less certain about factors or multiples. This incomplete knowledge of factors also makes it difficult for these students to find many different ways to multiply three or more whole numbers for a given product.

They are more likely to take random approaches to generate new expressions, rather than using factors or relationships they know.

Option: Assign the Practice activity.

Not Understanding the Mathematics
Students may have difficulty building different arrays for a given number and finding all the factors. These students may not have a solid conceptual understanding of multiplication and/or are unable to use an array as an area model for multiplication. Students are likely to "guess and check" when finding factors, and are generally unable to explain whether or not they know they have found all the factors. These students may also have difficulty identifying properties of numbers, solving number puzzles, and/or multiplying three or more whole numbers for a given product.

Option: Assign the Intervention activity.

Investigation 1 Quiz
In addition to your observations and students' work in Investigation 1, the Quiz (R1) can be used to gather more information.

Intervention

Multiples and Factors
Use anytime after Session 1.2.

Math Focus Points
- Determining whether one number is a factor or multiple of another

Vocabulary: factor, multiple
Materials: color tiles (80 per pair)

Tell students that today they are going to build arrays and use them to review factors and multiples. I want each of you to use some tiles to build an array that is 4 tiles wide.

Call on volunteers to describe the dimensions of their arrays as you draw each array on the board. Then ask students to tell you how many tiles there are in each array. Record the numbers on the board.

8, 20, 16, 32, 24, 12, 4, 40

What do you notice about all of these numbers?

Students might say:

"Those are numbers you get when you count by 4s."

That's right. All of these numbers are multiples of 4. Let's write them in order and fill in any of them that are missing. Record the sequence on the board, filling in any missing numbers up to 40.

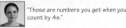

4, 8, 12, 16, 20, 24, __ , 32, __ , 40

Have students build an array and describe the dimensions for the missing numbers (28 and 36).

Have students repeat the procedure to generate multiples of 6 up to 60. Ask students to share their results.

Draw the following array on the board.

How are the 3 and the 6 related to 18? Numbers that can be multiplied to make 18 are called factors of 18. See if there are other ways to arrange the 18 tiles in a rectangle. Discuss students' results as you draw a 1 × 18 and a 2 × 9 array on the board. Remind students that for this activity, a 2 × 9 array is the same as a 9 × 2 array. We can use these arrays to list all the factors of 18. List the factors of 18 on the board as students call them out.

If time allows, have students use tiles to find all the factors of 12 and 20.

ELL English Language Learners
Use Repetition Students often confuse *multiple* and *factor* and need to build understanding. Ask questions such as, What is the difference between a *multiple* of 8 and a *factor* of 8? Emphasize these words as you pose questions, and listen for correct usage when observing students.

Additional Resource
Student Math Handbook pages 18–19

1 Mathematics in This Investigation gives an overview of the important mathematical ideas and skills students encounter during the Investigation.

2 Additional Resources provide teachers with information about pertinent Teacher Notes and/or Classroom Cases.

3 Performance descriptions assist teachers in determining differentiation activities based on observations of students throughout the Investigation and analyzing students' work.

4 The Quiz consists of 4 multiple-choice questions and 1 performance-based question. It can be used as an additional tool to help teachers identify students' levels of understanding of the mathematics in each Investigation.

5 Each differentiation activity is designed to be covered in 15 to 30 minutes in small groups, pairs, or as individuals.

Practice

 15 MIN INDIVIDUALS

Number Puzzles with 4 Clues
Use anytime after Session 1.3.

Math Focus Points
◆ Identifying prime, square, even, and odd numbers
◆ Determining whether one number is a factor or multiple of another

Vocabulary: odd number, square number, factor, multiple, prime number, composite number

Materials: color tiles (as needed), M31, R2

The puzzles in this activity incorporate the vocabulary terms. Review them with the class as needed.

Write the following clues on the board.

> Clue 1: This number is odd.
> Clue 2: This number is a square number.
> Clue 3: This number is a factor of 100.
> Clue 4: This number is less than 50.

Tell students that they need to find a number that fits all 4 clues. Allow them to use tiles or the 300 Chart (M31) as they consider the clues. Is it better to start with some clues than with others?

Students might say:

"I wouldn't start with Clue 1. I'd be listing odd numbers forever."

"I'd start with Clue 2 and list square numbers. But I wouldn't keep going because Clue 4 says that the number is less than 50."

Let's start with Clue 2 by listing the square numbers. Write them on the board as students call them out. We'll stop with 49 because Clue 1 says that the number is less than 50. Clue 1 tells us the number is odd, so which numbers should we cross out? Now all we have left are 1, 9, 25, and 49. Clue 3 says we're looking for a factor of 100. Which of these numbers work? *(1, 25)*

What if Clue 1 had said that the number was even? What would the answer be then? *(4)*

Distribute copies of Number Puzzles with 4 Clues (R2). Tell students that they should check that each number in their solution fits all 4 clues.

ELL English Language Learners

Provide a Word List Have students write the vocabulary terms on a sheet of paper. Review the meanings, then help students write examples for each. To check understanding, ask students to describe each term in their own words.

Additional Resource
Student Math Handbook pages 21–22

Extension

20 MIN PAIRS

Prime Factorization
Use anytime after Session 1.7.

Math Focus Points
◆ Determining the prime factorization of a number
Vocabulary: prime factorization
Materials: R3

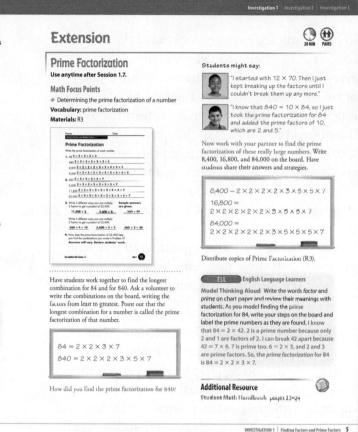

Have students work together to find the longest combination for 84 and for 840. Ask a volunteer to write the combinations on the board, writing the factors from least to greatest. Point out that the longest combination for a number is called the prime factorization of that number.

> $84 = 2 \times 2 \times 3 \times 7$
> $840 = 2 \times 2 \times 2 \times 3 \times 5 \times 7$

How did you find the prime factorization for 840?

Students might say:

"I started with 12 × 70. Then I just kept breaking up the factors until I couldn't break them up any more."

"I know that 840 = 10 × 84, so I just took the prime factorization for 84 and added the prime factors of 10, which are 2 and 5."

Now work with your partner to find the prime factorization of these really large numbers. Write 8,400, 16,800, and 84,000 on the board. Have students share their answers and strategies.

> $8,400 = 2 \times 2 \times 2 \times 2 \times 3 \times 5 \times 5 \times 7$
> $16,800 =$
> $2 \times 2 \times 2 \times 2 \times 2 \times 3 \times 5 \times 5 \times 7$
> $84,000 =$
> $2 \times 2 \times 2 \times 2 \times 2 \times 3 \times 5 \times 5 \times 5 \times 7$

Distribute copies of Prime Factorization (R3).

ELL English Language Learners

Model Thinking Aloud Write the words *factor* and *prime* on chart paper and review their meanings with students. As you model finding the prime factorization for 84, write your steps on the board and label the prime numbers as they are found. I know that 84 = 2 × 42. 2 is a prime number because only 2 and 1 are factors of 2. I can break 42 apart because 42 = 7 × 6. 7 is prime too. 6 = 2 × 3, and 2 and 3 are prime factors. So, the *prime factorization* for 84 is 84 = 2 × 2 × 3 × 7.

Additional Resource
Student Math Handbook pages 23–24

---

6 Activities can be used anytime after the session content is covered giving increased flexibility to teachers.

7 **Resource Masters** provide additional practice or are used as a recording sheet.

8 **ELL notes** provide teachers with suggestions to support students with language and vocabulary.

9 **Additional Resources** for students provide useful Student Math Handbook references or games to play for extra practice.

English Language Learners in the Math Classroom

Dr. Jim Cummins
University of Toronto

Research studies have demonstrated that English Language Learners (ELLs) generally pick up everyday conversational fluency within a year or two of starting to learn English. However, a much longer period (generally at least five years) is required for students to fully catch up to native speakers in academic language proficiency (e.g., vocabulary knowledge, reading and writing skills). In mathematics, ELL students often make good progress in acquiring basic computation skills in the early grades; however, they typically experience greater difficulty in carrying out word problems particularly as these problems become more complex linguistically in later grades.

Thus, ELL students are likely to require explicit *language* support within the classroom in order to achieve content standards in subject areas such as mathematics. Despite the fact that they have acquired conversational fluency in English together with basic mathematical vocabulary and computational skills, students may still experience gaps in their knowledge of more sophisticated vocabulary, syntax, and discourse features of mathematical language.

The linguistic challenges faced by ELL students in learning math reflect the fact that language is central to the teaching of virtually every school subject. The concepts embedded in the curriculum are inseparable from the language we use to teach these concepts to our students. For example, most mathematical problems require students to understand prepositions and logical relations that are expressed through language.

This fusion of language and content across the curriculum presents both challenges and opportunities in teaching ELL students. The challenges are to provide the instructional supports to enable ELL students to understand math content and carry out math tasks and operations. However, math instruction also provides teachers with the opportunity to extend ELL students' knowledge of language in ways that will significantly benefit their overall academic development. For example, as they learn mathematics, students are also learning that there are predictable patterns in how we form the abstract nouns that describe mathematical operations. Many of these nouns are formed by adding the suffix *–tion* to the verb, as in *add/addition, subtract/subtraction, multiply/multiplication,* etc. This knowledge can then be applied in other subject areas across the curriculum (e.g., science, language arts).

In building ELL supports for *Investigations*, we have been guided by *The Pearson ELL Curriculum Framework*, which incorporates the following five instructional principles central to teaching ELL students effectively.

1. Identify and Communicate Content and Language Objectives In planning and organizing a lesson, teachers must first identify what content and language objectives they want to communicate to students. The language objectives might include providing definitions, descriptions, examples, and visual supports for explaining vocabulary.

2. Frontload the Lesson Frontloading refers to the use of prereading or preinstructional strategies that prepare ELL students to understand new academic content. Frontloading strategies include activating prior knowledge, building background, previewing text, preteaching vocabulary, and making connections.

3. Provide Comprehensible Input Language and content that students can understand is referred to as comprehensible input. Teachers make use of nonlinguistic supports to enable students to understand language and content that would otherwise have been beyond their comprehension. Typical supports include visuals, models, and manipulatives.

4. Enable Language Production Language production complements comprehensible input and is an essential element in developing expertise in academic language. Use of both oral and written language enables students to solve problems, generate insights, express their ideas, and obtain feedback from teachers and peers.

5. Assess for Content and Language Understanding Finally, the instructional cycle flows into assessing what students have learned and then spirals upward into further development of students' content knowledge and language expertise.

These principles come to life in the *Differentiation and Intervention Guide* in the form of seven specific instructional strategies.

- **Model Thinking Aloud** When ELL students articulate their thinking processes through language, they are enabled to complete activities, identify gaps in their knowledge, and receive feedback from teachers. Teachers, however, must model this process in order for students to learn how to use it effectively. When modeling thinking aloud, it is important for teachers to use visuals and gestures.

- **Partner Talk** When it comes to working on a math activity of any kind, two heads are often better than one. Partner talk provides an audience for students' thinking aloud and an opportunity for the teacher to direct students to listen for particular vocabulary and linguistic structures as they engage in a task with their partner.

- **Provide a Word List** When students make a list of relevant vocabulary in a lesson with examples of how these words are used, it reinforces their knowledge of this vocabulary and provides an opportunity for teachers to monitor their understanding and provide additional explanation as needed. Paying special attention to homophones, such as *sum* and *some*, is particularly helpful for ELL students.

- **Provide Sentence Stems** Sentence stems provide support for ELL students to gain access to the sequence of steps in an activity, and they expand students' knowledge of how to communicate their thinking processes to the teacher and their peers.

- **Rephrase** Students struggling with vocabulary and language acquisition are often confused by extra details in word problems or overly wordy statements. Rephrasing statements in a different way that utilizes simpler language, shorter sentences, and eliminates unnecessary information helps students focus on and understand the important information needed to work through an activity.

- **Suggest a Sequence** Sequencing of steps is crucial to solving many math problems, and ELL students may need additional help in this process. Providing struggling ELL students with a sequence of steps to follow provides them with a guide for how to complete an activity or report their findings. When suggesting a sequence, be sure to use concise language.

- **Use Repetition** Repetition of instructions or explanations may also be required to enable ELL students to fully understand instruction. Because students are still in the process of learning English, they may need repetition, paraphrasing, or elaboration to understand teacher talk containing new vocabulary or structures.

Unit 1

Differentiation in Investigation 1

Mathematics in This Investigation

The mathematics focuses on using rectangular arrays to deepen understandings of factors, multiples, and other properties of numbers (even, odd, prime, composite, square). There is also a focus on multiplying three or more whole numbers for a given product (e.g., $18 = 2 \times 3 \times 3$).

Additional Resource: *Helping All Students Learn Multiplication Combinations,* pages 80–82 (See *Implementing Investigations in Grade 5*)

Understanding the Mathematics

Students easily build arrays and find all the factors of a given number. They are organized as they list factors and easily explain how they know they have found them all. They identify factors and multiples of numbers, know properties of numbers such as prime or square, and are able to use this information to solve the number puzzles. Students find many, or all, different ways to multiply three or more whole numbers for a given product. If given 18, students realize they can use 9×2 to create $3 \times 3 \times 2$. Students reason about multiplication expressions they've found for one number to find expressions for a number 10 times larger (e.g., $180 = 3 \times 3 \times 2 \times 10$).

Option: Assign the **Extension** activity.

Partially Understanding the Mathematics

Students build arrays, and understand what factors are, but are unable to find all the factors of given numbers. They are less organized—perhaps only listing one of the factors (e.g., if finding the factors of 42 they list 2, but not 21). They are unable to explain how they know they have found all the factors or offer only a partial explanation. When solving number puzzles, students are likely to know what square and prime numbers are, but are less certain about factors or multiples. This incomplete knowledge of factors also makes it difficult for these students to find many different ways to multiply three or more whole numbers for a given product.

They are more likely to take random approaches to generate new expressions, rather than using factors or relationships they know.

Option: Assign the **Practice** activity.

Not Understanding the Mathematics

Students may have difficulty building different arrays for a given number and finding all the factors. These students may not have a solid conceptual understanding of multiplication and/or are unable to use an array as an area model for multiplication. Students are likely to "guess and check" when finding factors, and are generally unable to explain whether or not they know they have found all the factors. These students may also have difficulty identifying properties of numbers, solving number puzzles, and/or multiplying three or more whole numbers for a given product.

Option: Assign the **Intervention** activity.

Investigation 1 Quiz

In addition to your observations and students' work in Investigation 1, the Quiz (R1) can be used to gather more information.

Name _____ Date _____

Number Puzzles and Multiple Towers

Quiz

Choose the correct answer.

1. Which multiplication combination is modeled by the array?

    A. $4 \times 8 = 32$ **C.** $4 \times 6 = 24$

    B. $4 \times 7 = 28$ **D.** $3 \times 7 = 21$

2. Which number is a prime number?

    A. 51   **B.** 49   **C.** 31   **D.** 1

3. Which shows all the factors of 42?

    A. 1, 2, 3, 6, 7, 14, 21, 42   **C.** 2, 3, 6, 7, 14, 21

    B. 1, 2, 3, 4, 6, 7, 42   **D.** 1, 6, 7, 42

4. Which number fits all four clues?
Clue 1: This number is a multiple of 3.
Clue 2: This number is even.
Clue 3: This number is a square number.
Clue 4: This number is less than 50.

    A. 9   **B.** 16   **C.** 30   **D.** 36

5. How can you use multiplication combinations for 24 to help you find multiplication combinations for 240?
Answers will vary. Review students' work.

Use after Session 1.7.   Unit 1 **R1**

Intervention

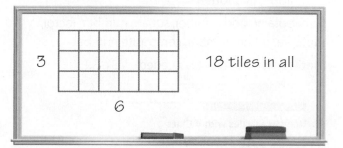

30 MIN   PAIRS

Multiples and Factors

Use anytime after Session 1.2.

Math Focus Points

◆ Determining whether one number is a factor or multiple of another

Vocabulary: factor, multiple

Materials: color tiles (80 per pair)

....

Tell students that today they are going to build arrays and use them to review factors and multiples. I want each of you to use some tiles to build an array that is 4 tiles wide.

Call on volunteers to describe the dimensions of their arrays as you draw each array on the board. Then ask students to tell you how many tiles there are in each array. Record the numbers on the board.

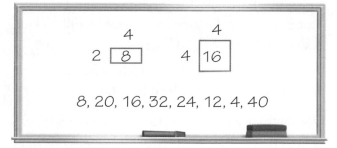

What do you notice about all of these numbers?

Students might say:

"Those are numbers you get when you count by 4s."

That's right. All of these numbers are multiples of 4. Let's write them in order and fill in any of them that are missing. Record the sequence on the board, filling in any missing numbers up to 40.

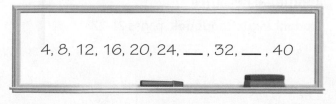

Have students build an array and describe the dimensions for the missing numbers (28 and 36).

Have students repeat the procedure to generate multiples of 6 up to 60. Ask students to share their results.

Draw the following array on the board.

How are the 3 and the 6 related to 18? Numbers that can be multiplied to make 18 are called factors of 18. See if there are other ways to arrange the 18 tiles in a rectangle. Discuss students' results as you draw a 1 × 18 and a 2 × 9 array on the board. Remind students that for this activity, a 2 × 9 array is the same as a 9 × 2 array. We can use these arrays to list all the factors of 18. List the factors of 18 on the board as students call them out.

If time allows, have students use tiles to find all the factors of 12 and 20.

ELL **English Language Learners**

Use Repetition Students often confuse *multiple* and *factor* and need to build understanding. Ask questions such as, **What is the difference between a *multiple* of 8 and a *factor* of 8?** Emphasize these words as you pose questions, and listen for correct usage when observing students.

Additional Resource

Student Math Handbook pages 18–19

Practice

Number Puzzles with 4 Clues

Use anytime after Session 1.3.

Math Focus Points

◆ Identifying prime, square, even, and odd numbers

◆ Determining whether one number is a factor or multiple of another

Vocabulary: odd number, square number, factor, multiple, prime number, composite number

Materials: color tiles (as needed), M31, R2

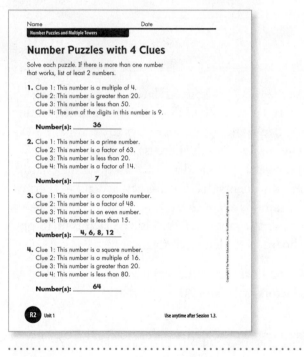

The puzzles in this activity incorporate the vocabulary terms. Review them with the class as needed.

Write the following clues on the board.

> Clue 1: This number is odd.
>
> Clue 2: This number is a square number.
>
> Clue 3: This number is a factor of 100.
>
> Clue 4: This number is less than 50.

Tell students that they need to find a number that fits all 4 clues. Allow them to use tiles or the 300 Chart (M31) as they consider the clues. Is it better to start with some clues than with others?

Students might say:

 "I wouldn't start with Clue 1. I'd be listing odd numbers forever."

 "I'd start with Clue 2 and list square numbers. But I wouldn't keep going because Clue 4 says that the number is less than 50."

Let's start with Clue 2 by listing the square numbers. Write them on the board as students call them out. We'll stop with 49 because Clue 4 says that the number is less than 50. Clue 1 tells us the number is odd, so which numbers should we cross out? Now all we have left are 1, 9, 25, and 49. Clue 3 says we're looking for a factor of 100. Which of these numbers work? *(1, 25)*

What if Clue 1 had said that the number was even? What would the answer be then? *(4)*

Distribute copies of Number Puzzles with 4 Clues (R2). Tell students that they should check that each number in their solution fits all 4 clues.

ELL **English Language Learners**

Provide a Word List Have students write the vocabulary terms on a sheet of paper. Review the meanings, then help students write examples for each. To check understanding, ask students to describe each term in their own words.

Additional Resource

Student Math Handbook pages 21–22

Extension

20 MIN PAIRS

Prime Factorization

Use anytime after Session 1.7.

Math Focus Points

◆ Determining the prime factorization of a number

Vocabulary: prime factorization

Materials: R3

Have students work together to find the longest combination for 84 and for 840. Ask a volunteer to write the combinations on the board, writing the factors from least to greatest. Point out that the longest combination for a number is called the prime factorization of that number.

$$84 = 2 \times 2 \times 3 \times 7$$
$$840 = 2 \times 2 \times 2 \times 3 \times 5 \times 7$$

How did you find the prime factorization for 840?

Students might say:

 "I started with 12 × 70. Then I just kept breaking up the factors until I couldn't break them up any more."

 "I know that 840 = 10 × 84, so I just took the prime factorization for 84 and added the prime factors of 10, which are 2 and 5."

Now work with your partner to find the prime factorization of these really large numbers. Write 8,400, 16,800, and 84,000 on the board. Have students share their answers and strategies.

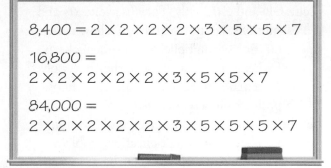

$$8,400 = 2 \times 2 \times 2 \times 2 \times 3 \times 5 \times 5 \times 7$$
$$16,800 =$$
$$2 \times 2 \times 2 \times 2 \times 2 \times 3 \times 5 \times 5 \times 7$$
$$84,000 =$$
$$2 \times 2 \times 2 \times 2 \times 2 \times 3 \times 5 \times 5 \times 5 \times 7$$

Distribute copies of Prime Factorization (R3).

ELL English Language Learners

Model Thinking Aloud Write the words *factor* and *prime* on chart paper and review their meanings with students. As you model finding the prime factorization for 84, write your steps on the board and label the prime numbers as they are found. I know that 84 = 2 × 42. 2 is a prime number because only 2 and 1 are factors of 2. I can break 42 apart because 42 = 7 × 6. 7 is prime too. 6 = 2 × 3, and 2 and 3 are prime factors. So, the *prime factorization* for 84 is 84 = 2 × 2 × 3 × 7.

Additional Resource

Student Math Handbook pages 23–24

Differentiation in Investigation 2

Mathematics in This Investigation

The mathematics focuses on fluently solving multiplication problems with 2-digit numbers, which includes multiplying by multiples of 10 and breaking the numbers up efficiently (e.g., breaking 27×12 into $(20 + 7) \times (10 + 2)$ or $(25 + 2) \times 12$).

Additional Resources: *Multiplication Strategies,* pages 161–162 (See Curriculum Unit 1); *First Steps in Creating the Mathematics Community,* pages 72–73 (See *Implementing Investigations in Grade 5*)

Understanding the Mathematics

Students have a strong understanding of the operation of multiplication and solve problems accurately and efficiently. They use contexts and representations, including arrays, to show their understanding of multiplication. Students keep track of what part of the problem they have solved and what remains to be solved. Students choose which problems in a set of cluster problems will best help them to solve the given multiplication problem. They solve a multiplication problem when given the first step. Students begin using different strategies to solve multiplication problems, based on the numbers given in the problem.

Option: Assign the **Extension** activity.

Partially Understanding the Mathematics

Students understand the operation of multiplication, but are working at becoming efficient and accurate. They may be depending on representations to help them solve the problem. Students break numbers apart in less than efficient ways (e.g., breaking 34 into $10 + 10 + 10 + 4$) and are likely to have trouble keeping track of the parts of the problem they have solved and what remains. Students can solve all the expressions in a set of cluster problems, but don't always see the relationships between those problems and how they relate to solving the final problem. They often struggle in solving a multiplication problem when given the first step.

Option: Assign the **Practice** activity.

Not Understanding the Mathematics

Students are still developing an understanding of the operation of multiplication. They are unable to solve most 2-digit multiplication problems because they don't multiply all the partial products, or they multiply incorrectly. They might be using repeated addition to solve problems. They often make mistakes when multiplying by multiples of 10. These students typically do not think about or see the relationships between numbers when solving problems (e.g., knowing how $5 \times 8 = 40$ helps them to know $5 \times 80 = 400$).

Option: Assign the **Intervention** activity.

Investigation 2 Quiz

In addition to your observations and students' work in Investigation 2, the Quiz (R4) can be used to gather more information.

Name _____ Date _____

Number Puzzles and Multiple Towers

Quiz

Choose the correct answer.

1. $9 \times 300 =$
  A. 27,000   **(B.)** 2,700   **C.** 2,100   **D.** 270

2. Which product is greater than 400×80?
  A. 700×8 **C.** 300×90
  (B.) 70×500 **D.** 40×800

3. $49 \times 24 =$
  A. 836   **B.** 1,076   **C.** 1,151   **(D.)** 1,176

4. Part of a student's solution for 28×67 is shown below.
  $20 \times 60 = 1{,}200$
  $20 \times 7 = 140$
  $8 \times 60 = 480$

  Which step should the student do next?
  (A.) 8×7 **B.** 20×6 **C.** 80×7 **D.** 2×6

5. Draw an array to show how to find 32×25.
  Answers will vary. Review students' work.

R4 Unit 1   Use after Session 2.7.

Intervention

30 MIN   PAIRS

Breaking Numbers Apart

Use anytime after Session 2.1.

Math Focus Points

◆ Solving 2-digit by 2-digit multiplication problems

◆ Creating a story problem represented by a multiplication expression

Vocabulary: break apart

....

Write 24 × 5 in vertical form on the board. Suppose I bought 5 cases of water. There are 24 bottles in a case. If I multiply 5 × 24, I'll know how many bottles I bought.

One way to make the problem easier is to break apart 24 into smaller numbers. What numbers could we use? Students are likely to suggest 10 + 10 + 4 and 20 + 4. Let's use 20 + 4 so we have fewer numbers to multiply. Draw the following diagram on the board.

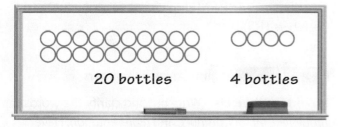

20 bottles   4 bottles

I'm buying 5 groups of 20 bottles and 5 groups of 4 bottles. I can draw it like this. Draw the following diagram.

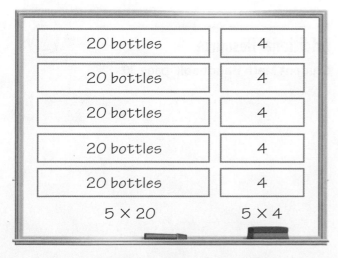

20 bottles	4
20 bottles	4
20 bottles	4
20 bottles	4
20 bottles	4
5 × 20	5 × 4

So now there are two parts to the problem. Work with your partner to figure out 5 × 20 and 5 × 4. Then add up your answers. How many bottles did I buy? Allow students to use other ways to break apart the problem, if desired.

Next, write 32 × 8 in vertical form on the board. Joshua bought 8 trays of pepper plants. Each tray has 32 plants. How can you use breaking apart to find how many pepper plants Joshua bought? Use a drawing to help you keep track of the problem.

Encourage students to use multiples of 10. As they work, ask them what part of the problem they have solved, and what they still have to solve.

Continue with problems such as 17 × 4, 27 × 6, and 41 × 7. Encourage students to create a story for each picture and draw pictures or an array to help.

ELL **English Language Learners**

Partner Talk Have one partner explain how to break apart 17 to find the product for 17 × 4. Then have the other partner explain how to break apart numbers to find 27 × 6. Students with limited language may write out number diagrams, such as 17 → 10, 7. Have students support one another to use the term *break apart* correctly once in a simple sentence, such as, "I can *break apart* 17 into 10 and 7."

Additional Resource

Student Math Handbook pages 16–17

Practice

20 MIN PAIRS

Multiplying 2-Digit by 2-Digit Numbers

Use anytime after Session 2.1.

Math Focus Points

◆ Solving 2-digit by 2-digit multiplication problems

◆ Describing and comparing strategies used to solve multiplication problems

Materials: R5

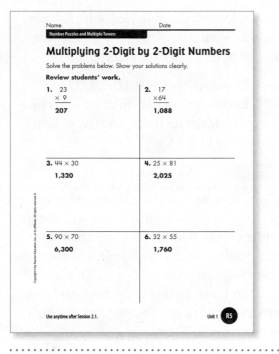

In this activity, students continue to practice, refine, and share strategies for multiplying 2-digit numbers by 2-digit numbers.

Write 33 × 25 on the board. Solve this problem, and then compare your solution with your partner. Whose solution do you like better? Why? Call on volunteers to share what they judge to be the better of the pair's two strategies, and why they liked it more.

Students might say:

"I like to multiply by tens. So I multiplied by 10 three times. But [Hana] did 30 × 25 = 750, and that's faster!"

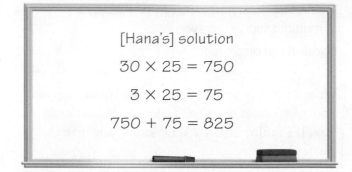

[Hana's] solution

30 × 25 = 750

3 × 25 = 75

750 + 75 = 825

Continue with problems such as 26 × 13, 31 × 21, and 29 × 22. Encourage students to try to solve the problems efficiently. Remind students that drawings can be used as a way to represent the problem. Have students share their strategies and solutions.

Distribute copies of Multiplying 2-Digit by 2-Digit Numbers (R5).

ELL English Language Learners

Provide a Word List Write out and clarify the words *multiplied, factors, product,* and *representation.* Have pairs explain their strategies using these words. Students with limited language may point to parts of their solution.

Additional Resource

Student Math Handbook page 30

Extension

25 MIN   PAIRS

Multiplication Compare with Digit Cards

Use anytime after Session 2.4.

Math Focus Points

◆ Solving 2-digit by 2-digit multiplication problems

◆ Comparing multiplication problems to determine which product is greater

Materials: Digit Cards (1 deck per pair), M46 (as needed), R6

Name   Date

Number Puzzles and Multiple Towers

***Multiplication Compare* with Digit Cards**

Write >, <, or = in each box. In the space to the right of each problem, write how you decided which product is greater. Challenge: Try to compare products without finding the exact answer to the multiplication problems.

Explanations will vary. Review students' work.

1. 31 × 36 > 22 × 42

2. 27 × 84 > 25 × 81

3. 16 × 69 = 48 × 23

4. 53 × 35 < 55 × 34

5. Use the digits 4, 1, 8, and 6 to make a 2-digit by 2-digit multiplication problem with the greatest product possible. How do you know this is the greatest product possible?
81 × 64 = 5,184; explanations will vary. Review students' work.

R6 Unit 1   Use anytime after Session 3.4.

In this activity, students play a variation of *Multiplication Compare* introduced in Session 2.3. In this version of the game, students use Digit Cards to generate 2-digit by 2-digit multiplication problems.

Distribute a deck of Digit Cards to each pair. Remove the "0" cards from your deck of Digit Cards. Mix the cards and give each player half of the deck. Explain that each player selects the top 4 cards and makes two 2-digit factors using the cards in the order in which they were drawn. Use the cards to demonstrate. I picked 3, 5, 7, and another 5. So I need to multiply 35 by 75.

Have pairs play this variation of *Multiplication Compare* for a given amount of time or until one player wins all the cards.

If you feel students need more of a challenge, have them play again, but this time allow them to use the four cards to make *any* 2-digit-by 2-digit multiplication problem. You might want to discuss some of the strategies students are using. I see you made 64 × 73. Why do you think that's the greatest possible product?

Students might say:

"I used estimation and figured 60 × 70 is 4,200. That's more than if I put the smaller digits in the tens place, like 36 × 47, which would only be about 2,000. So then I checked which had a greater product, 63 × 74 or 64 × 73."

Distribute copies of *Multiplication Compare* with Digit Cards (R6).

ELL **English Language Learners**

Provide a Word List Write the words *factors* and *product* on the board. Review the meanings. As partners discuss the game, encourage them to use these words. For example, "I made the *factors* 82 and 62. Then I got the *product* 5,084."

Additional Resource

Student Math Handbook page 30

Differentiation in Investigation 3

Mathematics in This Investigation

The mathematics focuses on using the relationship between multiplication and division to deepen understandings of the two operations and to solve division problems. There is also a focus on using multiples of 10 in solving division problems.

Additional Resource: *Student Grouping That Enhances Learning,* pages 77–79 (See *Implementing Investigations in Grade 5*)

Understanding the Mathematics

Students solve division problems efficiently by using either multiplication or division, often using the biggest reasonable chunks of numbers. They keep track of all parts of the problem and use clear and concise notation in their answers. Students see and use relationships on multiple towers or in division cluster problems to solve given division problems. Students understand how knowing the product of a number times a multiple of 10 helps them solve division problems more efficiently.

Option: Assign the **Extension** activity.

Partially Understanding the Mathematics

Students understand what the operation of division is, but have difficulty in consistently and efficiently solving division problems accurately. They understand and use the relationship between multiplication and division to solve problems. They may break the numbers into too many parts and struggle to keep track of all of their work. They understand how the 10th multiple of a number helps them solve division problems, but don't necessarily see the relationship to the 20th or 30th multiple.

Option: Assign the **Practice** activity.

Not Understanding the Mathematics

Students are likely to understand what the operation of division is, but they rely on using materials and on counting either the number of groups or the number in one group to solve division problems. When solving division problems, they only consider one group at a time, rather than considering how using multiples of that number would help them solve the problem more efficiently and accurately. They might be able to solve problems correctly using tools or drawings, but then have difficulty knowing what the answer is or using notation to communicate their solution.

Option: Assign the **Intervention** activity.

Investigation 3 Quiz

In addition to your observations and students' work in Investigation 3, the Quiz (R7) can be used to gather more information.

Name _____ Date _____

Number Puzzles and Multiple Towers

Quiz

Choose the correct answer.

1. 180 ÷ 18 =

   A. 5   **B.** 10   **C.** 20   **D.** 100

2. Which of the following is true?

   A. 200 ÷ 40 = 300 ÷ 50   **C.** 700 ÷ 90 < 400 ÷ 80

   B. 600 ÷ 80 < 720 ÷ 90   **D.** 500 ÷ 70 < 300 ÷ 60

3. 822 ÷ 35

   A. 32 R7   **B.** 23 R27   **C.** 23 R17   **D.** 22 R52

4. Part of a student's solution for 182 ÷ 14 is shown below.

   140 ÷ 14 = 10

   182 − 140 = 42

   42 ÷ 14 = 3

   Which step should the student do next?

   A. 10 + 3   **C.** 10 + 42 + 3

   B. 140 ÷ 2   **D.** 10 − 3

5. Describe how to use a multiple tower to find 330 ÷ 22.

   Answers will vary. Review students' work.

Use after Session 3.8.   Unit 1 R7

Intervention

30 MIN INDIVIDUALS

Building Multiple Towers

Use anytime after Session 3.2.

Math Focus Points

◆ Using and interpreting notation that represents division and relating division and multiplication notations (e.g., $170 \div 15 =$ _____ and _____ $\times 15 = 170$)

Vocabulary: multiple

Materials: R8

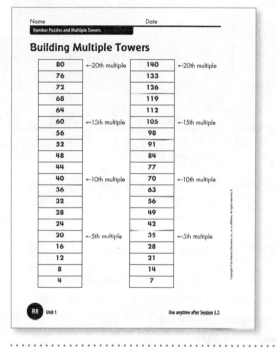

In this activity, students build a multiple tower using smaller numbers than in the sessions. Distribute copies of Building Multiple Towers (R8).

I want you to help me build a tower with multiples of 4. Use the first tower on your sheet.

Write 1×4. What's the first multiple of 4? Show students where to write 4 in the bottom box of the tower. Write 2×4. What's the second multiple of 4? Continue writing multiplication expressions to help students generate multiples of 4 until the 20 boxes of the tower are filled. If a student has trouble finding multiples greater than 10×4,

remind the student that he or she can add 4 to the previous multiple.

You can use your multiple tower to solve division problems. For example, how many 4s are there in 28? I can write that problem in two ways. Write the following equations on the board.

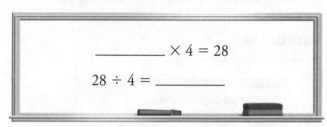

_____ $\times 4 = 28$

$28 \div 4 =$ _____

Find 28 on the tower. Which multiple is it? That tells you the answer is 7. 28 divided by 4 is 7.

Then write $64 \div 4 =$ _____ on the board. Ask students to use the tower to solve the problem.

Students might say:

"I found 64 on the tower. It's the 16th multiple of 4. So $64 \div 4 = 16$."

Have students solve other division problems with 4 as the divisor. Then repeat the activity by having students build a second tower with multiples of 7.

> **ELL** English Language Learners
>
> **Use Repetition** Reinforce understanding of ordinals as students refer to their multiple towers. Write the 1st through 20th ordinals on the board and review. Where is the 1st multiple of 4? Where is the 2nd multiple of 4? Continue through the 20th multiple of 4.

Additional Resource

Student Math Handbook page 20

Practice

20 MIN | PAIRS

Dividing by 2-Digit Numbers

Use anytime after Session 3.5.

Math Focus Points

◆ Solving division problems with 2-digit divisors

◆ Solving a division problem by breaking the dividend into parts

Materials: R9

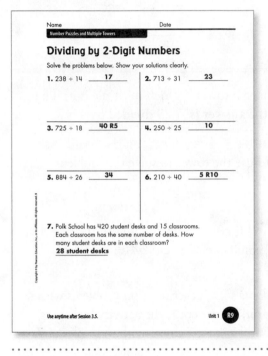

In this activity, students continue to practice and share strategies for dividing with 2-digit divisors. Write 917 ÷ 26 on the board. Solve this problem, and then compare your solution with your partner. Look among students' papers for strategies you may not have already discussed in class. Ask students to explain those strategies.

Students might say:

"First I made a multiple tower up to the 10th multiple. Then I kept subtracting the 10th multiple from 917. When I had only 137 left, I used the 5th multiple. I had 7 left for the remainder."

260	26)917	
234	−260	10 × 26
208	657	
182	−260	10 × 26
156	397	
130	−260	10 × 26
104	137	
78	−130	5 × 26
52	7	
26		35 R7

Repeat with other division problems, as needed.

Distribute copies of Dividing by 2-Digit Numbers (R9).

Partner Talk Write the words *dividend, divisor, quotient, multiple,* and *remainder* on the board. Have partners switch solutions. Have one partner determine the strategy used to find the solution. Then have the other partner verify. Students with limited language may label parts of the problem with these words.

Additional Resource

Student Math Handbook pages 38–39

Extension

30 MIN   PAIRS

Creating Cluster Problems

Use anytime after Session 3.5.

Math Focus Points

◆ Solving division problems with 2-digit divisors

◆ Solving a division problem by breaking the dividend into parts

In this activity, students consider which types of division cluster problems are most helpful to them. Then they create their own division cluster problems and share them with a partner.

Write the following on the board.

$$976 \div 23$$

Cluster 1	Cluster 2
$46 \div 23 = \underline{\hspace{1cm}}$	$10 \times 23 = \underline{\hspace{1cm}}$
$92 \div 23 = \underline{\hspace{1cm}}$	$20 \times 23 = \underline{\hspace{1cm}}$
$920 \div 23 = \underline{\hspace{1cm}}$	$40 \times 23 = \underline{\hspace{1cm}}$
$976 \div 23 = \underline{\hspace{1cm}}$	$976 \div 23 = \underline{\hspace{1cm}}$

Here are two different clusters that can help you divide 976 by 23. Take a few minutes to solve each cluster. Then tell me which one you like better.

Students might say:

"I like Cluster 2 better. It's always easier for me to turn division problems into multiplication problems."

"I'd rather use Cluster 1 because I can picture it better. I can take 920 out of 976. Then I still have to divide what's left, 56."

Write the following on the board.

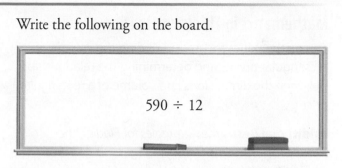

$$590 \div 12$$

Ask students to write a division cluster for the problem. Have students share and discuss their clusters. Do you like your cluster best, or is there another cluster you like better?

Ask each student to make up three division problems and a division cluster for each. Tell them not to write any answers. After giving students time to write their cluster problems, have partners exchange papers and solve one another's problems.

Did you and your partner write the same division clusters? Which cluster did you like the best? Why?

English Language Learners

Rephrase Students with limited language may have difficulty with the word *cluster*. Remind them that cluster problems are groups of related problems that use what they know to solve harder problems. As students work, guide them to think about the simpler problems by asking questions such as the following. Which of these do you already know the answer to? What do you still have to figure out? Rephrase questions referring to the cluster they like best by relating the simpler problems to the final problem, such as: Was it easier for you to find the answers to the problems in Cluster 1 or Cluster 2? How did those problems help you solve 976 ÷ 23?

Additional Resource

Student Math Handbook page 35

Differentiation in Investigation 1

Mathematics in This Investigation

The mathematics focuses on finding the volume of rectangular prisms and determining the relationships between the dimensions and volume of a rectangular prism.

Additional Resource: *Strategies for Finding the Number of Cubes in 3-D Arrays*, pages 113–114 (See Curriculum Unit 2)

Understanding the Mathematics

Students understand the structure of rectangular prisms. They are able to build a rectangular prism from a box pattern and to create a pattern for a given box. Students determine the number of cubes (volume) without having to build the actual rectangular prism. They use the dimensions of the rectangular prism to find the volume, usually multiplying the product of the dimensions of one layer (either vertical or horizontal) by the remaining dimension, and they are able to clearly communicate that strategy. Students understand that doubling one dimension of a rectangular prism doubles the volume.

Option: Assign the **Extension** activity.

Partially Understanding the Mathematics

Students have some difficulty in translating between finding the volume of a rectangular prism from a box pattern and designing a pattern for a given box. They often have to build the rectangular prism using connecting cubes, either to find the volume, or because they remain uncertain about strategies for finding volume. Students understand the relationship between the dimensions of the box and volume, but sometimes rely on counting (e.g., counting by ones to find the number of cubes in one layer, then skip counting the number of layers) to find the volume.

Option: Assign the **Practice** activity.

Not Understanding the Mathematics

Students may be able to build a rectangular prism from a box pattern, but often have great difficulty in designing a pattern for a given box. To find the volume, students need to build the rectangular prism and then count all the individual cubes. Students do not see the relationship between the dimensions and volume, so they struggle to find a general strategy for finding volume.

Option: Assign the **Intervention** activity.

Investigation 1 Quiz

In addition to your observations and students' work in Investigation 1, the Quiz (R10) can be used to gather more information.

Name _____ Date _____

Prisms and Pyramids

Quiz

Choose the correct answer.

1. How many cubes will fill the box shown at the right?

    A. 20   **C.** 120

    B. 100   **D.** 144

2. How many cubes will fill a box made with the pattern shown at the right?

    A. 94   **C.** 60

    B. 82   **D.** 12

3. What is the volume of a rectangular prism that is 4 units by 3 units by 8 units?

    A. 15 cubic units   **C.** 56 cubic units

    B. 30 cubic units   **D.** 96 cubic units

4. Martin has a box with dimensions $3 \times 3 \times 5$. What are the dimensions of a box that will hold twice as many cubes as Martin's box?

    A. $3 \times 6 \times 5$ **C.** $6 \times 6 \times 10$

    B. $3 \times 6 \times 10$ **D.** $9 \times 3 \times 5$

5. How many packages like the one shown at the right will fit in the box shown in Problem 1? Will the box be completely filled? Explain how you found your answer.

    12; no. Explanations will vary; review students' work.

R10 Unit 2   Use after Session 1.7.

Intervention

30 MIN   INDIVIDUALS

Boxes of Cubes

Use anytime after Session 1.2.

Math Focus Points

◆ Finding the volume of rectangular prisms

◆ Developing a strategy for determining the volume of rectangular prisms

Vocabulary: volume

Materials: connecting cubes (50 per student), tape, M11

....

Materials to Prepare: Use Three-Quarter-Inch Grid Paper (M11) to make a 3 × 4 × 3 box and a 2 × 5 × 4 box. Use very small pieces of tape to assemble the boxes so you can dismantle them later to reveal the patterns.

This activity provides extra support for students who have difficulty relating box patterns, prisms made of cubes, and volume.

Make one layer of cubes that has dimensions 3 × 4. Check that each student has connected the cubes. How many cubes did you use? *(12)* Let's put one layer in a box. Ask one of the students to place his or her layer in the 3 × 4 × 3 box.

If this is one layer, how many more layers do you think we'll need? How many cubes is that?

Ask another student to place his or her layer in the 3 × 4 × 3 box. How many cubes are in the box now? *(24)* How many more layers of cubes do we need? Ask another student to place his or her layer in the box.

How many cubes are in the box now? Lift each layer out of the box, asking students the total number of cubes each time. *(12, 24, 36)* How does knowing how many cubes are in one layer help us find the volume? What else do we need to know?

Disassemble the 3 × 4 × 3 box to reveal the pattern. Ask students to show where 3 × 4 shows up in the pattern and have a student shade it in on the pattern. So we know one layer is 3 × 4 or 12 cubes. How do we know how many layers there are?

Show students the 2 × 5 × 4 box and ask them to discuss with a partner how many cubes they think are in one layer of the box and how many layers there are.

Students might say:

"5, 10 so there are 10 cubes in the bottom layer. But I'm not sure how many layers there are."

Repeat the process used for the 3 × 4 × 3 box with the 2 × 5 × 4 box. It is important for students to see and count each layer of cubes and to continue thinking about how the number of cubes in one layer and the number of layers is connected to the volume of the box.

🔵 **ELL** 〉**English Language Learners**

Provide Sentence Stems Provide sentence stems to help students verbalize how to find the volume of a box. For example: To find the number of cubes in the bottom layer, I would _____. To find the number of cubes in the box, I would _____.

Additional Resource

Student Math Handbook pages 106–107

Practice

Volume of Boxes

Use anytime after Session 1.2.

Math Focus Points

◆ Designing patterns for boxes that hold a given number of cubes

◆ Finding the volume of rectangular prisms

Vocabulary: dimension, volume

Materials: scissors (as needed), tape (as needed), connecting cubes (as needed), M11 (several per group), R11

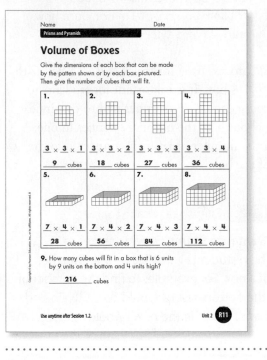

Have students work in groups of 4, or adjust the activity accordingly. Using Three-Quarter-Inch Grid Paper (M11), have the group draw patterns for boxes with dimensions $3 \times 6 \times 1$, $3 \times 6 \times 2$, $3 \times 6 \times 3$, and $3 \times 6 \times 4$. Assign a different box to each group member. For each pattern, use 3×6 as the dimensions of the bottom of the box.

Have students compare patterns. How are they similar? How are they different? If you assembled your box, what would be its volume? Compare your solution with everyone else's in your group. What do you notice?

Students might say:

"We all found the number of cubes that would fit in the bottom layer. That's 18, because $3 \times 6 = 18$. Then we multiplied 18 by the number of layers."

As students share their observations, write the following on the board.

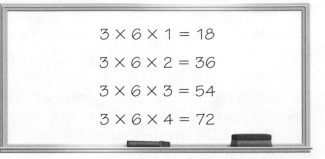

$$3 \times 6 \times 1 = 18$$
$$3 \times 6 \times 2 = 36$$
$$3 \times 6 \times 3 = 54$$
$$3 \times 6 \times 4 = 72$$

Students who show some uncertainty may need to assemble the boxes and fill them with cubes.

Suppose you have a box that is 8 units by 12 units on the bottom and 1 unit high. What is the volume? What if a box with the same-size bottom is 2 units high? What is the volume? What if the box is 3 units high? 4 units high? 10 units high?

Distribute copies of Volume of Boxes (R11).

English Language Learners

Suggest a Sequence Provide a format for sequencing the steps for finding volume. For example: *First,* I would multiply the dimensions on the bottom. *Next,* I would multiply by the number of layers. This gives the volume of the box.

Additional Resource

Student Math Handbook pages 106–107

Extension

30 MIN | PAIRS

New Dimensions

Use anytime after Session 1.5.

Math Focus Points

◆ Finding the volume of rectangular prisms

◆ Considering how the dimensions of a box change when the volume is changed (doubled, halved, or tripled)

Materials: R12

Ask students to find the volume of a $2 \times 3 \times 5$ box and record their work. Now, write the dimensions of three new boxes. For Box 1, double just 1 of the sides of the original box. For Box 2, double 2 sides. And for Box 3, double all 3 sides. Find the volume of each new box. How does it compare to the volume of the original box?

Students might say:

"The original box will hold 30 cubes. Box 1 will hold 60, which is twice as many. Box 2 will hold 120, which is 4 times as many. And Box 3 will hold 240. That's 8 times as many."

Start again using the dimensions of $3 \times 4 \times 6$ for the original box. Do the same relationships hold? Can you explain why this happens? Encourage students to discuss their ideas with a partner.

Students might say:

"If you double one side that's times 2. If you double another side it's times 2 again, so the volume is 4 times bigger."

Summarize students' findings on the board.

---

1 side doubled:
Volume is multiplied by 2

2 sides doubled:
Volume is multiplied by 2×2, or 4

3 sides doubled:
Volume is multiplied by $2 \times 2 \times 2$, or 8

Distribute copies of New Dimensions (R12).

ELL **English Language Learners**

Provide a Word List Help students make a list that includes the words *double*, *twice*, and *halve*. Read through the list with students and give examples to help students understand the meanings. Have students write an example or draw a picture for each. Allow students to refer back to this list as needed.

Additional Resource

Student Math Handbook page 108

Differentiation in Investigation 2

Mathematics in This Investigation

The mathematics focuses on measuring and finding the volume of large spaces, such as a classroom, using standard units of measure.

Understanding the Mathematics

Students understand the relationship between the linear measure of dimensions and cubic units. They are able to determine volume either by multiplying two dimensions to find one layer and then multiplying by the third dimension, or by multiplying all three measurements. They understand this product represents a different unit of measure—cubic units. They understand how changing the dimensions of a rectangular prism changes the volume.

Option: Assign the **Extension** activity.

Partially Understanding the Mathematics

Students understand the concept of volume and can find volume without building the entire 3-D array, but they often use cubes to build either one layer, or at least to find each dimension. They do not completely understand the relationship between the linear measurements and volume, and they seem uncertain about which units to use for measuring length and which to use for measuring volume. When measuring the classroom, they may not realize they have to measure three different dimensions.

Option: Assign the **Practice** activity.

Not Understanding the Mathematics

Students are still working on understanding the concept of volume as the space that a solid occupies. They struggle to understand how using linear measurements of the dimensions in the room helps them to determine the volume. They do not understand the distinction between the units used to measure linear dimensions and the units used to measure volume. When asked to find the volume of a smaller rectangular prism, these students often need to build the 3-D array out of cubes, and then count all the cubes.

Option: Assign the **Intervention** activity.

Investigation 2 Quiz

In addition to your observations and students' work in Investigation 2, the Quiz (R13) can be used to gather more information.

Name _____ Date _____

Prisms and Pyramids

Quiz

Choose the correct answer.

1. Tamira found the volume of her classroom and said it was 230. What unit of measure did she use?

  A. centimeters **C.** cubic centimeters

  B. square meters **D.** cubic meters

2. Which is the length of an edge of a cubic meter?

  A. 1 centimeter **C.** 2 meters

  B. 1 meter **D.** 3 meters

3. Which is the volume of a rectangular prism with dimensions 3 centimeters by 5 centimeters by 8 centimeters?

  A. 16 cubic centimeters **C.** 120 cubic centimeters

  B. 40 cubic centimeters **D.** 240 cubic centimeters

4. Which is the volume of a room that is 8 meters long, 8 meters wide, and 3 meters high?

  A. 384 cubic meters **C.** 186 cubic meters

  B. 192 cubic meters **D.** 48 cubic meters

5. What are the dimensions of a box that has half the volume of the box pictured?

  Answers will vary.
  Review students' work.

10 cm   4 cm   4 cm

Use after Session 2.4. Unit 2 **R13**

Intervention

30 MIN   INDIVIDUALS

Filling Our Classroom with Cubes

Use anytime after Session 2.3.

Math Focus Points

◆ Finding the volume of a large space, such as the classroom, using cubic meters

◆ Describing and defending measurement methods

Vocabulary: volume, length, width, height, cubic meter

Materials: connecting cubes (as needed), M11

....

Materials to Prepare: Use Three-Quarter-Inch Grid Paper (M11) to make an open box that corresponds to the dimensions of your classroom. For example, if your classroom is 8 meters by 12 meters by 3 meters, you need to make an open box that is 8 units by 12 units by 3 units. (If your classroom is irregularly shaped, make a model of the largest rectangular section of the room.)

This activity helps students visualize filling their classroom with cubic meters.

When we find the volume of our classroom, we want to know how many cubes will fit in it. We can't really fill our classroom with cubes, so instead we have to *picture* how many cubes would fit.

Show the model of the classroom to students. Remember when we measured our classroom? We found that the floor is [8] meters by [12] meters, so I made the bottom of the model [8] units by [12] units. Our classroom is about 3 meters high, so I made my model 3 units high.

Let's use our model to help us picture the cubes in our classroom. How many cubes can we fit along the length of the model? To reinforce that a length of [12] units corresponds to [12] cubes, have a student place the [12] cubes along the length of the floor of the model. Make sure the cubes are connected so they fit. How many cubes can we fit

along the width of the classroom? Have a student fit the cubes accordingly.

How many cubes can we fit in one layer on the floor? How can you figure that out without using cubes to make the entire layer?

What is the height of the model? So how many layers will fill the model to the top? Show this with cubes. How can you figure out how many cubes altogether will fill the model?

You figured out how many cubes would fill the model without actually filling it with cubes. How can this help you figure out how many cubic meters would fill our classroom?

Students might say:

"You figure it out the same way. You just multiply the length by the width to count the cubes that would cover the floor. Then you multiply by the height to count the cubes in all the layers."

Suggest a Sequence Provide a format for sequencing the steps to help students explain how to find the number of cubic meters in the classroom. For example: *First,* I would find the number of cubic meters in the bottom layer. *Then,* I would multiply that number by the number of layers. This gives the number of cubic meters in the classroom.

Additional Resource

Student Math Handbook pages 109–110

Practice

25 MIN   GROUPS

Volume in Cubic Centimeters

Use anytime after Session 2.1.

Math Focus Points

◆ Determining the volume, in cubic centimeters, of a small prism

Vocabulary: volume, cubic centimeter

Materials: small boxes like those that might hold jewelry (several per group), centimeter cubes (as needed), R14

Name _____ Date _____

Prisms and Pyramids

Volume in Cubic Centimeters

Picture centimeter cubes along the length, width, and height of each of the 2 boxes shown below. Write the dimensions of the boxes.

1 cubic centimeter

1.

__6__ cm long   __5__ cm wide   __3__ cm high

What is the volume of this box? Show how you found the answer.

Volume: 90 cubic centimeters; review students' work.

2.

__4__ cm long   __4__ cm wide   __7__ cm high

What is the volume of this box? Show how you found the answer.

Volume: 112 cubic centimeters; review students' work.

R14 Unit 2   Use anytime after Session 2.1.

This activity provides extra practice for finding volume in cubic centimeters.

Use one box for a demonstration. When we find the volume of a box, we want to know how many cubes will fit in it. Today we are going to use centimeter cubes. Hold up a centimeter cube. So our volume will be measured in cubic centimeters.

Show students how to pack the box tightly with cubes. Tell them that for today's problems they need not worry about small amounts of leftover space.

How can you find the number of cubes in the box? Do you need to count them all?

Students might say:

"You could just count how many fill the bottom layer and then multiply by the number of layers that would fit. You could stack up cubes to figure out how many layers would fit."

"You could count how many cubes fit the length, how many fit the width, and how many fit the height. Then multiply the three numbers."

Empty the box. Can someone demonstrate how to use cubes to measure the length, width, and height of the box without filling the entire box?

Give each group several small boxes. Have students label them 1, 2, 3, and so on. Have students work independently to find the volume of each box in cubic centimeters and record their work. Then have them compare their results with the other group members and attempt to resolve any discrepancies.

Distribute copies of Volume in Cubic Centimeters (R14).

ELL) **English Language Learners**

Partner Talk Have ELL pairs discuss the following questions to give them practice with English. How many cubic centimeters will fit in Box 1? How do you know? Beginning English Language Learners may only be able to respond using short phrases like "I counted." Encourage more proficient speakers to use the words *volume, length, width,* and *height.*

Additional Resource

Student Math Handbook page 109

Extension

30 MIN   PAIRS

Growing Boxes

Use anytime after Session 2.4.

Math Focus Points

◆ Considering how the dimensions of a box change when the volume is changed (doubled, halved, or tripled)

Materials: R15

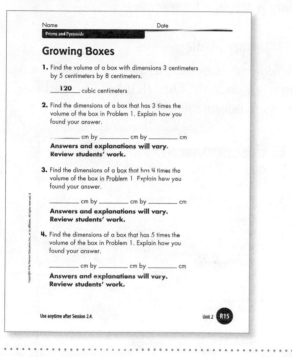

Ask students to find the volume of a box that is 2 centimeters by 3 centimeters by 5 centimeters and record their work. Now, work by yourself and find the dimensions of a new box that has 3 times the volume of the original box. Then compare your solution with your partner's. Did you find the same-size box?

Students might say:

"The volume of the original box is 30 cubic centimeters. So the new box has to hold 90 cubic centimeters. Any three numbers with a product of 90 will work. I used 3, 3, and 10. My new box is 3 centimeters by 3 centimeters by 10 centimeters."

"All I did was triple one of the dimensions. I replaced the 2 centimeters with 6 centimeters. So my new box is 6 centimeters by 3 centimeters by 5 centimeters."

Next, ask students to find a new box with a volume equal to 4 times the volume of the original box. Have students share their results and explain their strategies. If students need an additional challenge, tell them the dimensions can include fractions or decimals.

Original box: 2 cm × 3 cm × 5 cm

Volume of original box: 30 cubic centimeters

Volume of new box: 120 cubic centimeters

New boxes: 3 cm × 4 cm × 10 cm

2 cm × 3 cm × 20 cm

8 cm × 3 cm × 5 cm

Distribute copies of Growing Boxes (R15).

ELL **English Language Learners**

Rephrase When you ask students to *find the dimensions of a box,* you can rephrase this as *find the length, find the width,* and *find the height of a box.*

Additional Resource

Student Math Handbook page 108

Differentiation in Investigation 3

Mathematics in This Investigation

The mathematics focuses on finding volume relationships between prisms and pyramids (and between cylinders and cones) that have the same base and height.

Understanding the Mathematics

Students understand that if a prism and pyramid have the same dimensions for the base and height, the prism has 3 times the volume of the pyramid. They know the same idea is also true of cylinders and cones. Students use this information to build a prism that has 3 times the volume of a given pyramid. They come up with a strategy to compute the volume of pyramids. They find the volume of the related rectangular prism and divide by 3.

Option: Assign the **Extension** activity.

Partially Understanding the Mathematics

Students understand that there is some sort of relationship between the volume of prisms and pyramids with the same base and height, but they are unsure as to exactly what the relationship is. They are less certain of the relationship between the volume of a cylinder and a cone that have the same dimensions. Students might use trial and error to build shapes that have the same volume but not necessarily the same base and height. They find the volume of these related shapes, but use the physical materials rather than calculating the volume from the dimensions.

Option: Assign the **Practice** activity.

Not Understanding the Mathematics

Students are beginning to understand the concept of volume, but are overwhelmed with all the different solids, so they do not see the relationship between the related shapes. They might over-generalize and think they can multiply the 3 dimensions of a rectangular pyramid to find volume, not realizing that their answer is the volume of the related prism.

Option: Assign the **Intervention** activity.

Investigation 3 Quiz

In addition to your observations and students' work in Investigation 3, the Quiz (R16) can be used to gather more information.

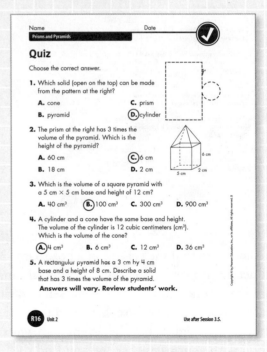

Intervention

Volume of Prisms and Pyramids

Use anytime after Session 3.3.

Math Focus Points

◆ Demonstrating the 3:1 relationship between rectangular prisms and pyramids with the same base and height

Vocabulary: prism, pyramid

Materials: rice (about 1 cup per pair); trays (1 per pair); student-made solids A, B, I, J, K (from Session 3.1); M26 and M29–M30 (as needed)

. . . .

Materials to Prepare: Gather students' paper models assembled in Session 3.1 for solids A, B, I, J, and K, or construct them yourself from the patterns (M26, M29, M30). Be sure the edges are taped securely. Each pair of students will need one set of these solids, rice, and a tray.

This activity focuses on the volume relationship between prisms and pyramids.

Begin with solids A and B. Be sure students can identify each solid. Review their properties as needed. Fill the pyramid with rice. Then pour the rice from the pyramid into the prism. Did the prism fill completely? Fill the pyramid again, and then pour the rice from the pyramid into the prism. Keep doing this until the prism is filled.

Ask each pair how many times they poured rice from the pyramid to the prism, to the closest whole number. Establish that it took 3 times, and that means the prism has 3 times the volume of the pyramid.

Tell students to empty Shapes A and B. Look at these two shapes, and especially their dimensions. How are they the same? How are they different? Give students a minute or two to discuss this, and then ask for responses. Students should place the objects base-to-base to show the bases are the same, as well as having some way to show the heights are the same.

Have students repeat the experiment using solids I and K. As before, ask students to compare the dimensions of the shapes and demonstrate that the bases and heights of Solids I and K are the same.

Repeat the experiment one more time using solids I and J. This time did you find that the volume of the prism is 3 times the volume of the pyramid?

Students might say:

"No. We had to pour from the pyramid into the prism into the prism 6 times."

Ask students to compare the dimensions of the shapes. Let's see what else is different this time. They should notice that while the heights of solids I and J are the same, the bases are *not* the same.

⬛ **ELL** ⬛ **English Language Learners**

Provide a Word List Write the words *base, height, prism* and *pyramid* on chart paper. Read each word with students and draw a picture for each one. Post the list in the classroom for reference.

Additional Resource

Student Math Handbook pages 111–114

Practice

15 MIN   PAIRS

Using the Three-to-One Relationship

Use anytime after Session 3.4.

Math Focus Points

◆ Finding volume, in cubic centimeters, of prisms, pyramids, cylinders, and cones

Materials: student-made solids A and B (from Session 3.1), completed volume chart (from Session 3.4), R17

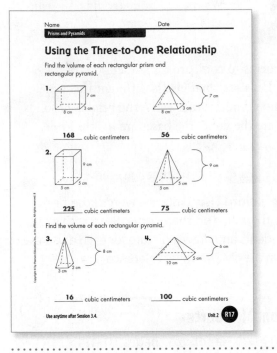

Hold up models of solid A and solid B. How can I find the volume of the prism without actually filling it with cubes, sand, or rice?

Students might say:

"We have to figure out how many cubes are in one layer, and how many layers. Then, we multiply the numbers."

What about the pyramid? Is there also a way to find the volume of the pyramid without actually filling it with cubes, sand, or rice? Talk to your partner and see if you can come up with a way.

Students might say:

"The chart shows that sometimes the volume of the prism is 3 times the pyramid. So, maybe divide by 3?"

Yes, that will work as long as the prism and pyramid have the same base *and* the same height. Draw the following figures on the board. Have students work together to determine the volume of each one.

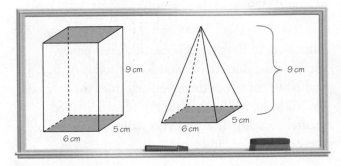

Distribute copies of Using the Three-to-One Relationship (R17).

ELL **English Language Learners**

Partner Talk Review the words *pyramid* and *prism* with students. Have ELL pairs answer the following question to give them practice with English. **How did you find the volume of the solids I drew on the board?** Beginning English Language Learners may only be able to use short phrases or point to parts of the figures. More proficient speakers can add information to help create a more detailed answer.

Additional Resource

Student Math Handbook pages 111–114

Extension

20 MIN PAIRS

Pyramids in Architecture

Use anytime after Session 3.4.

Math Focus Points

◆ Finding volume, in cubic centimeters, of prisms, pyramids, cylinders, and cones

Materials: calculators (optional), R18

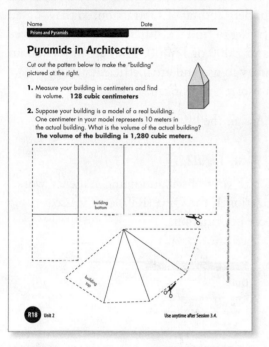

....

Remind students of the work they've been doing to find the volumes of rectangular prisms and pyramids that have the same base and height.

Today, we're going to do some more work with prisms and pyramids. Instead of measuring in centimeters though, we're going to use some actual buildings. There is a pyramid at the Louvre, which is a famous museum in Paris, France. It's a square pyramid that is about 21 meters high, and has a base edge of 35 meters. Work with a partner to figure out what its volume is.

Give students a few minutes to work together to find a solution. Allow students to use calculators if they want. Ask a pair of students to share their solution.

Students might say:

"At first we didn't think we had enough information, because there were only 2 measurements. Then we remembered it was a square pyramid. We multiplied 35 × 35 and got 1,225, and multiplied that by 21, and that was 25,725 cubic meters. That's the volume of a prism, not a pyramid, so we divided by 3 and got 8,575 cubic meters."

Ask if anyone has questions or got a different answer. Discuss as needed.

Let's solve one more problem. The Memphis Pyramid is a square pyramid that is 98 meters high, and has a base edge of 183 meters. Is its volume going to be greater or less than the volume of the pyramid at the Louvre? How do you know? Students should easily recognize it's going to be greater because of the dimensions. Just looking at the dimensions, about how much bigger do you think it's going to be? Talk to a partner. Give students time to work to find the volume of the Memphis Pyramid. Ask pairs to share their solution, and discuss as needed.

Distribute copies of Pyramids in Architecture (R18).

ELL English Language Learners

Model Thinking Aloud Draw a labeled sketch of the Louvre Pyramid. Model your thinking for finding its volume. The Louvre Pyramid is a *square* pyramid. So the length *and* the width of the base measure 35 meters. First, I found the area of the base: 35 × 35 = 1,225. Then, I multiplied by the height, 21, to get 25,725. Since it is a pyramid, I divided by 3. So, the volume is 8,575 cubic meters.

Additional Resource
Student Math Handbook pages 111–114

Differentiation in Investigation 1

Mathematics in This Investigation

The mathematics focuses on using place-value relationships and multiples of 10 (including multiples of 100 and 1,000) to add and subtract 4-digit numbers.

Additional Resource: *What's the "Difference"?,* pages 87–88 (See *Implementing Investigations in Grade 5*)

Understanding the Mathematics

Students read and write numbers to 100,000. They fluently add and subtract multiples of 10, 100, and 1,000. They understand the place-value relationships between 10, 100, 1,000, and 10,000. Students understand that to find the difference between a given number and 1,000, or 10,000, they can either add up or subtract to find the answer. They use large, efficient chunks of numbers in finding their solution, and they keep track of their work. Students use clear and concise notation to show their thinking.

Option: Assign the **Extension** activity.

Partially Understanding the Mathematics

Students read and write numbers in the 1,000s, but are not consistently able to do so with larger numbers. They have some understanding of the place-value relationships between 10, 100, and 1,000. Students have difficulty adding and subtracting multiples of 100, particularly when the sum affects the thousands place (e.g., 847 + 400, 3,789 + 500). Students understand difference, but when asked to find the difference between a given number and 1,000 or 10,000, they usually add up in ways that are not efficient (e.g., adding only 100 or 1,000 at a time) and often make place-value type errors. They also lose track of their work and are unable to identify their answer.

Option: Assign the **Practice** activity.

Not Understanding the Mathematics

Students are still developing their understanding of place-value concepts to 1,000 and are confused when asked to consider place-value relationships. Given a number, students may correctly add or subtract 10 or 100, but they have difficulty adding or subtracting multiples of 10 or 100 or using those ideas to solve addition and subtraction problems. They do not have a strong understanding of subtraction, so they struggle trying to find the difference between a given number and 1,000 or 10,000. They are unsure about what strategy to use and are inefficient as they attempt to solve the problem.

Option: Assign the **Intervention** activity.

Investigation 1 Quiz

In addition to your observations and students' work in Investigation 1, the Quiz (R19) can be used to gather more information.

Name _____ Date _____

Thousands of Miles, Thousands of Seats ✓

Quiz

Choose the correct answer.

1. Which shows 100,000 in words?
   A. one thousand
   B. ten thousand
   C. one hundred thousand
   D. one million

2. Start at 4,260. How many steps is it to 10,000?
   A. 14,260   **B.** 6,740   **C.** 5,740   **D.** 1,240

3. Which number is between 27,401 and 27,500?
   A. 27,385   **B.** 26,450   **C.** 27,505   **D.** 27,490

4. 6,211 + 5,000 =
   A. 6,216   **B.** 6,261   **C.** 6,711   **D.** 11,211

5. How can finding 3,649 + 200 help you find 3,649 + 230?
   Answers will vary. Review students' work.

Use after Session 1.5.   Unit 3 **R19**

Intervention

30 MIN · INDIVIDUALS

Using Related Problems

Use anytime after Session 1.4.

Math Focus Points

◆ Solving addition and subtraction problems with large numbers by focusing on the place value of the digits

....

This activity provides extra support for students who have difficulty working with numbers in the thousands. Students will solve sets of related 2- and 3-digit problems.

Write the following problems on the board.

yellow flowers		red flowers		
40	+	30	=	_____
40	+	32	=	_____
45	+	32	=	_____

Suppose you pick 40 yellow flowers and 30 red flowers. How many flowers do you pick in all? Which problem on the board can you use to find the answer? What's the answer? Write 70 as the answer to the first problem.

Suppose you pick 2 more red flowers. Now, how many flowers do you pick altogether? Which problem on the board can you use to find the answer? Can you use the answer to the first problem to find 40 + 32? Will the new answer be larger or smaller than 70? How much larger? How do you know? So, how much is 40 + 32? Write 72 as the answer to the second problem.

Suppose you pick 5 more yellow flowers. Now, which problem on the board can you use to find how many flowers you pick altogether? How can you use the answer to the second problem to find 45 + 32?

Students might say:

"45 + 32 is just like 40 + 32, except the first number is 5 bigger. So that makes the answer 5 bigger. I just add 5 to 72. 72 + 5 = 77. That's my answer!"

Write another set of related problems on the board, as shown below.

cars in parking lot		cars leaving parking lot		
500	−	200	=	_____
500	−	210	=	_____
500	−	216	=	_____

Present a story about cars in a parking lot. As in the first example about flowers, adjust the story and develop a line of questioning that emphasizes how the second and third problems are each related to the one that precedes it.

Present several other sets of related problems with 2- and 3-digit numbers. See if students can extend their reasoning to solve sets of related problems in the thousands.

ELL) **English Language Learners**

Rephrase As volunteers explain their thinking, pause and rephrase as necessary so that the explanations are understood by all students. [Nora] says she subtracted because cars are *leaving* the parking lot. That's why we see the minus sign. [Tyler] says 300 − 10 is 290. The answer to the first problem, 300, helped him solve the new problem.

Additional Resource

Student Math Handbook page 6

Practice

20 MIN   PAIRS

Missing Numbers

Use anytime after Session 1.3.

Math Focus Points

◆ Finding the difference between a number and 10,000

Materials: R20

Name _____ Date _____

Thousands of Miles, Thousands of Seats

Missing Numbers

Solve each set of problems.

1. 2,840 + __160__ = 3,000
   2,840 + __2,160__ = 5,000
   2,840 + __3,160__ = 6,000
   2,840 + __7,160__ = 10,000

2. 4,010 + __990__ = 5,000
   4,010 + __1,990__ = 6,000
   4,010 + __3,990__ = 8,000
   4,010 + __5,990__ = 10,000

3. 1,375 + __625__ = 2,000
   1,375 + __3,625__ = 5,000
   1,375 + __5,625__ = 7,000
   1,375 + __8,625__ = 10,000

4. 6,808 + __3,192__ = 10,000

5. 3,333 + __6,667__ = 10,000

6. 5,519 + __4,481__ = 10,000

R20 Unit 3   Use anytime after Session 1.3.

Write the following problems on the board.

$$1,465 + \underline{\hspace{1cm}} = 2,000$$

$$1,465 + \underline{\hspace{1cm}} = 3,000$$

$$1,465 + \underline{\hspace{1cm}} = 5,000$$

$$1,465 + \underline{\hspace{1cm}} = 10,000$$

Here are some *How Many Steps* problems. First, you have to figure out how many steps it is from 1,465 to 2,000. Then you'll find how many steps it is to 3,000, then to 5,000, and finally to 10,000. Solve the set of problems by yourself and then compare your work to your partner's. Can someone explain how your *partner* solved the problems?

Students might say:

"[Alicia] likes doing jumps on a number line. The first jump is 535. The second jump is 1,000 farther. That's 1,535. The third jump is another 2,000 farther. That's 3,535. And the last jump is 5,000 past that, which is 8,535."

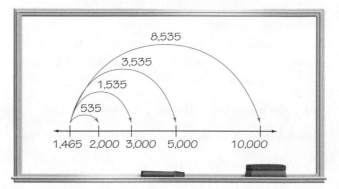

Have a discussion with students about how these problems are related. If we wanted to find out how many steps it was from 1,465 to 10,000, how do these problems help? Could [Alicia] combine some of [her] jumps? Have a discussion about using the biggest numbers possible when solving problems.

Let's solve another problem. How many steps is it from 4,785 to 10,000? Give students time to answer the question and discuss student strategies.

Distribute copies of Missing Numbers (R20).

ELL English Language Learners

Provide Sentence Stems Provide sentence stems to help students explain their work. For example: To find the number of steps from 1,465 to 2,000, I _____. To find the number of additional steps to 3,000, I _____.

Additional Resource

Student Math Handbook
Game: *Close to 1,000* SMH G2
Materials: Digit Cards, M7

Extension

Close to 10,000

Use anytime after Session 1.4.

Math Focus Points

◆ Solving addition and subtraction problems with large numbers by focusing on the place value of the digits

◆ Finding the difference between a number and 10,000

Materials: Digit Cards (1 deck per pair), M8 (as needed), R21

Name _____ Date _____
Thousands of Miles, Thousands of Seats

Close to 10,000

Circle the sum that is closer to 10,000.

1. 6,217 + 3,684   [6,248 + 3,671]
2. 5,506 + 4,125   [5,506 + 4,512]
3. [1,097 + 8,896]   1,967 + 8,089
4. [2,602 + 7,351]   6,205 + 3,721
5. 4,008 + 6,119   [4,019 + 6,018]
6. [3,890 + 6,143]   1,343 + 6,609

7. Use the cards below to make two 4-digit numbers with a sum as close as possible to 10,000. Complete the number sentence.

Answers will vary. Review students' work.

| 8 | 4 | 6 | 0 | 1 |

| 4 | 0 | 9 | 5 | 7 |

_____ _____ + _____ _____ = _____

Use anytime after Session 1.4.   Unit 1 **R21**

In this activity, students play a variation of *Close to 1,000* introduced in Session 1.3. In this version, you'll find number combinations close to 10,000. When you play *Close to 10,000*, you'll get ten digit cards. You need to use any eight of them to make two 4-digit numbers. The sum should be as close as you can get to 10,000.

On the board, draw the cards pictured in the following display. Have pairs discuss possible addends. Record some suggestions and related scores.

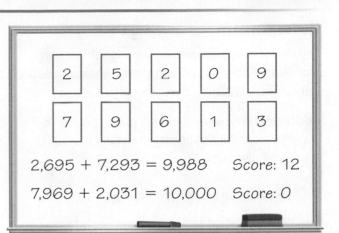

| 2 | 5 | 2 | 0 | 9 |
| 7 | 9 | 6 | 1 | 3 |

2,695 + 7,293 = 9,988   Score: 12
7,969 + 2,031 = 10,000   Score: 0

Have students play five rounds. They should record the rounds and the scores on a separate sheet of paper. If you feel students need more of a challenge, have them use 12 cards per hand and play *Close to 100,000*.

Distribute copies of *Close to 10,000* (R21).

ELL ▸ **English Language Learners**

Partner Talk Provide a place-value chart for reference and have pairs answer the following question. How do you decide what digits go in the thousands, hundreds, tens, or ones places as you make numbers? Beginning English Language Learners may only be able to respond with short phrases or point to parts of the place-value chart. More proficient speakers can add information to help create a more detailed answer. As partners play the game, check that students are correctly saying the numbers they make with the Digit Cards.

Additional Resource

Student Math Handbook pages 6–7

Differentiation in Investigation 2

Mathematics in This Investigation

The mathematics focuses on solving subtraction problems efficiently and accurately. Analyzing and using different subtraction strategies is also a focus.

Additional Resource: *Describing, Comparing, and Classifying Subtraction Strategies,* pages 123–124 (See Curriculum Unit 3)

Understanding the Mathematics

Students solve subtraction problems accurately, efficiently, and flexibly. They easily add and subtract multiples of 10 and 100. Students have a strong understanding of subtraction, and when given different starts for solutions, they efficiently solve the remainder of the problem. They are able to keep track of their work and often solve large parts of the problem mentally. Students use different strategies when solving subtraction problems, based on the numbers involved.

Option: Assign the **Extension** activity.

Partially Understanding the Mathematics

Students usually solve subtraction problems accurately. They add and subtract multiples of 10 and 100 correctly, but they do not see how that skill might help them more efficiently solve other subtraction problems. Students have one strategy they consistently use. They usually keep one number whole and subtract in parts, but they tend to break the number into too many parts, causing them to lose track of the problem or to make computational mistakes. When given different starts, students may or may not solve the remainder of the problem. They either turn the start into the strategy they normally use, or don't see how a different strategy can be used to solve the problem.

Option: Assign the **Practice** activity.

Not Understanding the Mathematics

Students struggle to solve subtraction problems correctly. They are still developing an understanding of place value for subtraction concepts, and often make place-value type errors when trying to add or subtract multiples of 10 or 100. They usually attempt to use different strategies for solving subtraction problems but often carry out the strategy without any understanding. They lose track of the problem they are trying to solve or of the steps in their solution. They often make large computational errors, usually based on place-value ideas.

Option: Assign the **Intervention** activity.

Investigation 2 Quiz

In addition to your observations and students' work in Investigation 2, the Quiz (R22) can be used to gather more information.

Name _____ Date _____ ✔

Thousands of Miles, Thousands of Seats

Quiz

Choose the correct answer.

1. 647 − 271 =
   A. 376   **B.** 366   **C.** 276   **D.** 266

2. Yumiko is driving from Chicago to Phoenix, which is 1,800 miles. She has driven 871 miles. How many miles is she from Phoenix?
   A. 929 miles   **C.** 1039 miles
   B. 939 miles   **D.** 1071 miles

3. 2,790 − 2,406 =
   A. 284   **B.** 384   **C.** 394   **D.** 396

4. Talisha is using the U.S. algorithm to subtract 734 − 506.

   $$\begin{array}{r} 7\overset{2}{\cancel{3}}\overset{1}{4} \\ -\ 506 \end{array}$$

   What does the little 1 represent?
   A. 1 hundred   **B.** 4 ones   **C.** 1 one   **D.** 1 ten

5. Joshua is solving the problem 3,851 − 396. Here is how he began his solution:

   3,851 − 400 = 3,451

   What should Joshua do next? Explain your answer.
   Answers will vary. Review students' work.

R22 Unit 3   Use after Session 2.5.

Intervention

⏱ **30 MIN**   👤 **INDIVIDUALS**

Subtracting in Parts
Use anytime after Session 2.3.

Math Focus Points

◆ Analyzing and using different subtraction strategies

This activity focuses on the subtraction strategy of subtracting in parts.

Olivia is driving 915 miles to visit her cousin. If she has driven 628 miles, how many miles does she still have to drive? What problem do I need to solve? Write 915 − 628.

One way to do this subtraction problem is to subtract 628 miles in smaller parts. How could we break the 628 into smaller parts? Students are likely to suggest a number of ways.

Let's use the biggest chunk we can. Subtract 915 − 600. You can use a number line to help you keep track of your work. Draw a number line with just the number 915 labeled.

Help students draw and label a backwards jump of 600 from 915. Some students may need to make jumps of 100, which is fine. Help them record their work.

How much of the problem have we solved? How many more miles has Olivia driven? How can we break up the 28? Now, let's subtract the 20. Find 315 − 20. Again, help students draw and label this on a number line and record the subtraction. Some students may subtract 10 and 10, rather than 20.

Now how far has Olivia driven? How much more do we need to subtract? Ok, let's subtract 8. Find 295 − 8. Have students draw this final jump on the number line and record the subtraction. We've subtracted the entire 628 miles. How many miles does Olivia still have to drive?

$$
\begin{array}{r}
915 \\
-\ 600 \\
\hline
315 \\
-\ 20 \\
\hline
295 \\
-\ 8 \\
\hline
287
\end{array}
$$

Using the same context, give students several other 3-digit subtraction problems to solve by subtracting in parts.

If students seem comfortable with 3-digit subtraction, repeat the activity using 4-digit numbers.

ELL ▸ English Language Learners

Rephrase Many English Language Learners have difficulty with story problems containing extra information. Rephrase story problems so that only the necessary information is included. For example: Olivia is driving 915 miles. She has driven 628 miles. How many more miles does she need to drive?

Additional Resource 📖
Student Math Handbook page 10

Practice

20 MIN INDIVIDUALS

Solving Subtraction Problems

Use anytime after Session 2.4.

Math Focus Points

◆ Analyzing and using different subtraction strategies

Materials: R23

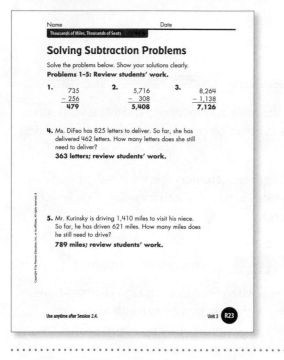

Name _____ Date _____

Thousands of Miles, Thousands of Seats

Solving Subtraction Problems

Solve the problems below. Show your solutions clearly.
Problems 1–5: Review students' work.

1. 735
  − 256

  479

2. 5,716
  − 308

  5,408

3. 8,264
  − 1,138

  7,126

4. Ms. DiFeo has 825 letters to deliver. So far, she has delivered 462 letters. How many letters does she still need to deliver?
363 letters; review students' work.

5. Mr. Kurinsky is driving 1,410 miles to visit his niece. So far, he has driven 621 miles. How many miles does he still need to drive?
789 miles; review students' work.

Use anytime after Session 2.4.   Unit 3 R23

Write 763 − 428 on the board. Who can make up a story for this problem?

Students might say:

"There were 763 people in the park. 428 people left the park. How many people are still in the park?"

Ask students to solve the problem.

Choose a solution where students could be using the strategy more efficiently, such as the one shown at the right. Have volunteers record their work on the board and discuss the solutions.

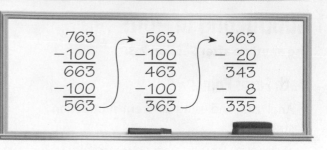

$$763 \atop -100 \atop \overline{663}$$ $$\rightarrow$$ $$563 \atop -100 \atop \overline{463}$$ $$\rightarrow$$ $$363 \atop -20 \atop \overline{343}$$

$$663 \atop -100 \atop \overline{563}$$ $$463 \atop -100 \atop \overline{363}$$ $$343 \atop -8 \atop \overline{335}$$

Let's look at this solution. Is the answer correct? Is there a way we could use this strategy, but use fewer steps? Talk to a partner.

Students might say:

"Yes. You could combine some of those 100s or all of them! 763 − 400 is 363."

Next, ask students to solve 3,536 − 729, share their solutions, and have a similar discussion. Encourage students to think about using fewer steps when solving subtraction problems.

Distribute copies of Solving Subtraction Problems (R23).

ELL **English Language Learners**

Use Repetition As students explain their work, pose questions using short, simpler forms with which ELL students may be more familiar. How did you start the problem? Why did you subtract in smaller parts? How do you know what your answer is?

Additional Resource

Student Math Handbook pages 10–13

Extension

15 MIN   PAIRS

Equivalent Subtraction Problems

Use anytime after Session 2.1.

Math Focus Points

◆ Solving whole-number addition and subtraction problems efficiently

Materials: R24

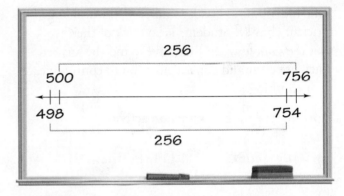

In this activity, students use and analyze subtraction strategies that involve writing equivalent problems.

Write 754 − 498 on the board. Work with your partner. What are some ways you could change this into an easier problem by changing one or both numbers? Take students' suggestions and record them on the board. Draw attention to the solution that shows 756 − 500 = 256, or suggest it yourself.

Let's look at a solution in which both numbers were changed, 756 − 500 = 256. This is an *equivalent* problem. That means the new problem has the same answer as the original problem. How do you think these numbers were chosen? Why do you get an equivalent problem?

Students might say:

"It's easy to subtract hundreds, and 498 is really close to 500. So you add 2 to 498, and then you have to add 2 to 754, also."

"You can see why this works on a number line. When you do 754 − 498 on a number line, you're figuring out the distance between the two numbers. If you shift one number up by 2, you have to shift the other number up by 2 so that the distance doesn't change."

Distribute copies of Equivalent Subtraction Problems (R24).

ELL | **English Language Learners**

Partner Talk Have pairs answer the following question. What math words can you use to describe how you solved the problem? As partners discuss the problems, listen for the word *equivalent*. For example, a student might say, *I added 2 to both numbers to make an equivalent problem.* Beginning English Language Learners may pair with a partner from the same language group to speak using their native language.

Additional Resource

Student Math Handbook page 12

Differentiation in Investigation 3

Mathematics in This Investigation

The mathematics focuses on accurately and efficiently solving addition and subtraction problems with 4- and 5-digit numbers.

Understanding the Mathematics

Students fluently solve addition and subtraction problems involving large numbers. They use a strong understanding of place-value relationships and of the operations to solve problems. They recognize addition or subtraction situations, and choose a strategy that is based on the numbers involved in the problem. Students are able to use multiples of 10, 100, and 1,000 to break numbers apart into large, efficient chunks. Students keep track of their work so that they know when they have found the answer. They use clear and concise notation to communicate their thinking.

Option: Assign the **Extension** activity.

Partially Understanding the Mathematics

Students correctly solve 3- and 4-digit addition and subtraction problems but often are not efficient in the strategies they use. They also have a difficult time solving problems with larger numbers. They break the numbers up into too many pieces, which sometimes causes them to make computational errors or to lose track of the part of the problem they still have to solve. Students usually use only one strategy for addition or subtraction, regardless of the numbers involved in the problem. They often have a difficult time keeping track of their work, particularly with subtraction problems. They are uncertain if they've finished the problem, and are unsure about recognizing their answer.

Option: Assign the **Practice** activity.

Not Understanding the Mathematics

Students correctly solve 3-digit addition problems but have difficulty solving addition problems with larger numbers. They sometimes solve 3-digit subtraction problems correctly, but they have trouble doing so. Given a number, these students might be able to add and subtract 10 and 100, but they struggle to use multiples of 10 and 100. They don't necessarily connect this skill with efficiently solving addition and subtraction problems.

Option: Assign the **Intervention** activity.

Investigation 3 Quiz

In addition to your observations and students' work in Investigation 3, the Quiz (R25) can be used to gather more information.

Name _____ Date _____

Thousands of Miles, Thousands of Seats

Quiz

Choose the correct answer.

1. Which sum is closest to 7,500?
   - **A.** 2,845 + 4,369
   - **B.** 6,420 + 984
   - **C.** 1,999 + 5,603
   - **D.** 3,905 + 3,730

2. 14,862 − 10,000 =
   - **A.** 14,852   **B.** 14,762   **C.** 13,862   **D.** 4,862

3. 49,812 + 12,409 =
   - **A.** 52,221   **B.** 62,203   **C.** 62,221   **D.** 62,321

4. There are 28,617 students at Central Prairie University. 25,438 students live on the campus. How many students do not live on the campus?
   - **A.** 3,279 students   **C.** 3,189 students
   - **B.** 3,253 students   **D.** 3,179 students

5. Avery is solving 27,705 − 25,680. He is adding up from 25,680 to 27,705. His first step is shown below. Show how Avery could complete his solution.

   25,680 + 20 = 25,700

   Answers will vary. Review students' work.

Use after Session 3.5.   Unit 3 **R25**

Intervention

20 MIN | PAIRS

Multistep Problems

Use anytime after Session 3.3.

Math Focus Points

◆ Interpreting and solving multistep problems

Materials: R26

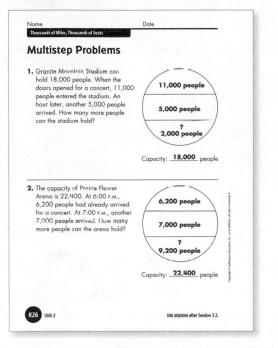

Name _____ Date _____

Thousands of Miles, Thousands of Seats

Multistep Problems

1. Granite Mountain Stadium can hold 18,000 people. When the doors opened for a concert, 11,000 people entered the stadium. An hour later, another 5,000 people arrived. How many more people can the stadium hold?

11,000 people
5,000 people
?
2,000 people

Capacity: **18,000** people

2. The capacity of Prairie Flower Arena is 22,400. At 6:00 P.M., 6,200 people had already arrived for a concert. At 7:00 P.M., another 7,000 people arrived. How many more people can the arena hold?

6,200 people
7,000 people
?
9,200 people

Capacity: **22,400** people

R26 Unit 3 — Use anytime after Session 3.3.

....

In this activity, students use simple diagrams to represent the parts of multistep problems. The numbers in these problems involve only multiples of 100 and 1,000 so that students can give more thought to interpreting and representing the problem. Distribute copies of Multistep Problems (R26).

Read through the first problem with students. The circle can be used to represent the entire stadium. How many people can the stadium hold? Show students where to record the *capacity* below the circle. The circle is split into parts so you can show the different groups of people in the stadium. How many people entered the stadium when it opened? Write 11,000 people in one part of the circle. How many people came an hour later? Write 5,000 people in another part of the circle.

Is the stadium filled yet? How do you know? The empty part of the circle represents how many more people it would take to fill the stadium. Write a question mark in that part of the circle. That part of the circle is what you have to figure out to solve the problem. Talk to your partner. Figure out how many more people it would take to fill the stadium.

After students solve the problem, have them explain their solutions. Have them write the answer in the part of the circle with the question mark. What should the three parts of the circle add up to? Let's check that.

Have pairs work together to solve the second problem, completing the diagram as they did earlier.

ELL **English Language Learners**

Rephrase Some English Language Learners may struggle with the word *stadium*. Explain that stadiums are places where sporting events and concerts are held. If needed, use another word with which students may be more familiar, such as *building*.

Additional Resource

Student Math Handbook pages 10–11

Practice

20 MIN | PAIRS

Addition and Subtraction with Large Numbers

Use anytime after Session 3.2.

Math Focus Points

◆ Solving addition and subtraction problems with large numbers by focusing on the place value of the digits

Materials: R27

Name _____ Date _____

Thousands of Miles, Thousands of Seats

Addition and Subtraction with Large Numbers

Solve the problems below. Show your solutions clearly.

1. 2,410 + 31,500 = **33,910**
Review students' work.

2. 51,727 − 14,300 = **37,427**
Review students' work.

3. 42,628 + 20,315 = **62,943**
Review students' work.

4. 32,860 − 7,085 = **25,775**
Review students' work.

5. A stadium has 28,940 seats. 25,256 seats are filled. How many seats are empty?
3,684; review students' work.

6. There are 14,602 adults at a concert and 8,099 children. How many people are at the concert?
22,701; review students' work.

Use anytime after Session 3.2.   Unit 3 **R27**

In this activity, students continue to practice and share strategies for adding and subtracting large numbers.

Write 24,620 − 9,275 on the board. Solve this problem and show your solution clearly so others can understand it. Compare your solution with your partner's solution. Ask a volunteer to explain his or her *partner's* solution and show the partner's work on the board.

Students might say:

"[Felix] kept adding up until he got to 24,620. He added big amounts first, like 10,000 and 5,000. Then when he was getting close, he added smaller amounts so he wouldn't go over. To get his final answer, he had to add up all those amounts."

$$
\begin{array}{r}
9{,}275 \\
+\ 10{,}000 \\
\hline
19{,}275 \\
+\quad 5{,}000 \\
\hline
24{,}275 \\
+\qquad 300 \\
\hline
24{,}575 \\
+\qquad\ 25 \\
\hline
24{,}600 \\
+\qquad\ 20 \\
\hline
24{,}620
\end{array}
\qquad
\begin{array}{r}
10{,}000 \\
5{,}000 \\
300 \\
25 \\
+\qquad 20 \\
\hline
15{,}345
\end{array}
$$

Have students solve 13,408 + 38,256 and compare their solution with their partner's. Again, ask a volunteer to explain his or her *partner's* solution.

Distribute copies of Addition and Subtraction with Large Numbers (R27).

ELL **English Language Learners**

Partner Talk Have pairs compare their solutions and then answer the following questions. Did you get the same answer? How do you know if your answer is correct? Beginning English Language Learners may only be able to respond using short phrases like "yes" or "no." Encourage more proficient speakers to add information to help create a more detailed answer.

Additional Resource

Student Math Handbook pages 8–13

Extension

30 MIN   PAIRS

Keeping Score with Negative Numbers

Use anytime after Session 3.1.

Math Focus Points

◆ Solving addition and subtraction problems with large numbers by focusing on the place value of the digits

Materials: Digit Cards (1 deck per pair), M16 (1 per pair), M17 (as needed)

In this activity, students play the variation of *Close to 7,500* shown on M17. In this version of the game, positive and negative numbers are used to keep score.

Write the following on the board.

$$\underline{4}\,\underline{3}\,\underline{2}\,\underline{5} + \underline{3}\,\underline{1}\,\underline{8}\,\underline{1} = \underline{} \qquad \text{Score}$$
$$\underline{1}\,\underline{0}\,\underline{7}\,\underline{2} + \underline{6}\,\underline{4}\,\underline{1}\,\underline{9} = \underline{} \qquad \underline{}$$

Here are two rounds of *Close to 7,500*. What is the sum in each round? Fill in the sums, 7,506 and 7,491.

Today, we are going to use a new method to keep score. When the sum is *greater* than 7,500, write your score with a plus sign. Since the first sum is 6 more than 7,500, the first score is +6. Write +6 for the first score.

When the sum is *less* than 7,500, write your score with a minus sign. The second score is 9 less than 7,500, so the second score is −9. Write −9 for the second score.

You still want your score to be as close to 0 as possible. If you had +6 and −9, what would be your total score? Give students a short amount of time to find the answer. Most students are able to figure out the answer is −3. If students have

difficulty, providing a story context might help. For example: If you owe someone $9.00 and have $6.00, how much do you still owe?

So, if your score is −3, what number should you try to make on your next round? Does this new rule change the game? How?

Suppose the scores for five rounds of *Close to 7,500* are +4, −1, +7, −7, and +2. Work with your partner and find the total score. *(+5)*

Have pairs play the game using positive and negative numbers to keep score. The player whose total score is closer to zero is the winner.

ELL) **English Language Learners**

Provide Sentence Stems Provide sentence stems to help students explain their work. For example: In round 1, my score was _____. In round 2, my score was _____. My total score is _____. Next round I want to get _____.

Additional Resource

Student Math Handbook pages 10–13

Differentiation in Investigation 1

Mathematics in This Investigation

The mathematics focuses on using 10 × 10 grids to identify equivalent fractions and percents and to understand the meaning of fractions and percents.

Additional Resource: *Visualizing Fractions and Percents,* pages 147–149 (See Curriculum Unit 4)

Understanding the Mathematics

Students understand fractions as being equal parts of a whole or of a group. They understand that "percent" means "out of 100." They are able to find equivalent fractions and percents through reasoning and using the 10 × 10 grids. Students use fraction-percent equivalents they know to find other equivalents (e.g., knowing $\frac{3}{8}$ is $37\frac{1}{2}\%$ because $\frac{3}{8}$ is $\frac{1}{4}$ plus $\frac{1}{8}$). Students correctly solve problems about fractions and percents by using equivalents and reasoning.

Option: Assign the **Extension** activity.

Partially Understanding the Mathematics

Students have a basic understanding of fractions and percents, but struggle to use those relationships to find equivalents. They rely on shading the 10 × 10 grids to find equivalent percents. They use some simple relationships (e.g., $\frac{1}{4}$ is $\frac{1}{2}$ of $\frac{1}{2}$, so $\frac{1}{4}$ is 25%), but they don't extend that thinking to eighths, or the relationships between thirds and sixths. Students are able to solve some problems about fractions and percents, but often use grids or other representations.

Option: Assign the **Practice** activity.

Not Understanding the Mathematics

Students are still working on their understanding of fractions as being equal parts of a whole or of a group. They do not understand what percents are, usually thinking of them as whole numbers. When students work with drawings to find equivalent fractions, they often don't use equal-sized pieces, and this leads to inaccurate solutions. Students do not see the relationships between fractions such as halves, fourths, and eighths, so they treat each problem as a new idea. They struggle to solve problems involving fractions and percents.

Option: Assign the **Intervention** activity.

Investigation 1 Quiz

In addition to your observations and students' work in Investigation 1, the Quiz (R28) can be used to gather more information.

Name _____ Date _____

What's That Portion?

Quiz

Choose the correct answer.

1. Which does **not** describe the shaded part of the grid?
   A. $\frac{4}{10}$ C. 40%
   B. 4%   D. $\frac{2}{5}$

2. 7% =
   A. $\frac{7}{10}$ B. $\frac{1}{7}$ C. $\frac{7}{100}$ D. $\frac{1}{700}$

3. $\frac{5}{8}$ =
   A. $12\frac{1}{2}\%$ B. 58 %   C. $62\frac{1}{2}\%$ D. $66\frac{2}{3}\%$

4. On a test of 25 problems, Rachel solved 80% correctly. How many problems did Rachel solve correctly?
   A. 20   B. 16   C. 15   D. 8

5. Shade 25% of the grid.
   Answers will vary. Review students' work.

R28   Unit 4   Use after Session 1.5.

Intervention

30 MIN INDIVIDUALS

Understanding Fractions and Percents

Use anytime after Session 1.3.

Math Focus Points

◆ Finding fractional parts of a rectangular area

◆ Identifying fraction and percent equivalents through reasoning about representations and known equivalents and relationships

Vocabulary: half, percent, fourth, eighth

Materials: scissors, R29

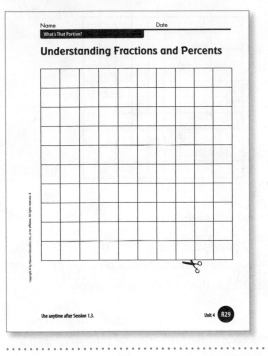

This activity reinforces the percent equivalents for $\frac{1}{2}$, $\frac{1}{4}$, $\frac{3}{4}$, and $\frac{1}{8}$ for students who have difficulty relating percents and fractions.

Ask students to cut out the 10 × 10 grid on Understanding Fractions and Percents (R29). Then, have them carefully fold the grid in half, but not along the diagonal. Tell them to make a sharp crease and then open the paper.

How many little squares are there in the grid? How many of them are in one half of the grid? Fifty percent means fifty out of one hundred. Fifty percent is also another way to describe one half. Write $\frac{1}{2} = 50\%$. What if we wanted to find $\frac{1}{4}$ of this grid? How should we fold our grid?

Have students fold the grid back in half and then in half again so that the fold lines are perpendicular. How many equal parts do we have now? How many little squares are in $\frac{1}{4}$? Write $\frac{1}{4} = 25\%$.

How many squares are in $\frac{2}{4}$? What is the fraction equivalent? Write $\frac{2}{4} = \frac{1}{2} = 50\%$. How many squares are in $\frac{3}{4}$? Write $\frac{3}{4} = 75\%$. What if we wanted to find eighths? How should we fold our grid? How many squares is that?

Help students count the number of squares and half-squares in a one-eighth region. $12\frac{1}{2}$ out of 100 little squares fill $\frac{1}{8}$ of the grid. How do you write that as a percent? Write $\frac{1}{8} = 12\frac{1}{2}\%$.

ELL **English Language Learners**

Provide a Word List Write the words *half, percent, fourth,* and *eighth* on chart paper. Help students list numerical examples and draw related diagrams to serve as a reminder of each word's meaning. Post the word list in the classroom for reference.

Additional Resource

Student Math Handbook pages 46, 48–49

Practice

25 MIN PAIRS

Finding Fraction and Percent Equivalents

Use anytime after Session 1.4.

Math Focus Points

◆ Finding a percentage of a rectangular area

◆ Identifying fraction and percent equivalents through reasoning about representations and known equivalents and relationships

Vocabulary: percent, equivalent

Materials: M9 (as needed), T43, R30

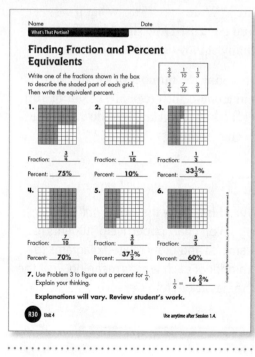

. . . .

Using the transparency of 10 × 10 Grids (T43), divide one of the grids with thick lines and shade it as shown below to show $\frac{1}{8}$.

Look at the thicker lines that divide up the grid. What fraction of the grid is shaded? Talk to your partner. Let's use this grid to find the percent equivalent for $\frac{1}{8}$. How did you figure it out?

Students might say:

"We counted all the little squares and half-squares in the shaded part. It came out to $12\frac{1}{2}$. It's $12\frac{1}{2}$%."

Divide another grid and shade it as shown below. What fractions and percents can you figure out from the way I've drawn this grid?

Students might say:

"Those look like thirds. If you count the squares carefully you can tell that $\frac{1}{3}$ is $33\frac{1}{3}$% and $\frac{2}{3}$ is $66\frac{2}{3}$%."

Distribute copies of Finding Fraction and Percent Equivalents (R30).

━━━━━━━━━━━━

ELL ⟩ **English Language Learners**

Provide a Word List Write the words *percent*, *equivalent*, and % on the board. Have students copy this list onto a sheet of paper and write examples for each. As students discuss their work, listen for correct usage of fraction names and of these words.

━━━━━━━━━━━━

Additional Resource

Student Math Handbook pages 47–49

Extension

Write Your Initials

Use anytime after Session 1.3.

Math Focus Points

◆ Finding a percentage of a rectangular area

Materials: colored pencils, M9, T43

Materials to Prepare: Draw one of your initials (or the letter M for *math*) on the transparency of 10 × 10 Grids (T43). Make certain to shade only full squares and half-squares.

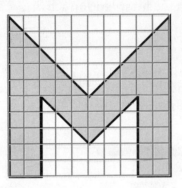

This activity incorporates percents beyond those discussed in the sessions. **How can you figure out what percent of the grid is shaded?**

Students might say:

"Count all the little squares that are shaded. First count all the whole squares. Then count the half-squares. I can check them off as I count so I don't lose track."

Ask a volunteer to count the squares and then give the percent.

Give each student a copy of 10 × 10 Grids (M9). Use two of the grids to draw your two initials. You can be as creative as you want and may use colored pencils. But you may only shade full squares and half-squares.

When you're finished, exchange papers with your partner. Figure out what percent of each grid is shaded and write that beneath the grid. Also, write one or more equivalent fractions for each percent. Then exchange papers again, and check each other's work.

After students are finished, discuss the activity. Does it look like some letters were harder to make than others? Which used up a greater percent of the grid? Did anyone discover any "shortcuts" for determining the percent of the grid that is shaded?

Students might say:

"The A had symmetry. So I just counted half of the squares and then doubled that number."

"I divided the T into two rectangles, and I multiplied to find the number of squares in each rectangle."

ELL **English Language Learners**

Rephrase Have students write their first name and last name. Point to each as you say *first name* or *last name*. The first name is also known as the *given name*, and the last name is known as the *family name*. Be aware that in some cultures, the given name traditionally comes after the family name. Check that students understand what the word *initial* means. Rephrase this as the *first letter of your name*.

Additional Resource

Student Math Handbook pages 47–49

Differentiation in Investigation 2

Mathematics in This Investigation

The mathematics focuses on using fraction equivalents, fraction-percent equivalents, and relationships of fractions to compare and order fractions.

Understanding the Mathematics

Students compare and order fractions through reasoning about fraction equivalents and relationships. Students' strategies to compare fractions include using 0, $\frac{1}{2}$, and 1 as landmarks; using percent equivalents; using related denominators and equivalents; and using their understanding of the relationship between the numerator and denominator. Most students reason numerically, but when using drawings, they are careful to make certain that their wholes are the same size and that the fractions are based on equal pieces. Students correctly answer problems involving comparing fractions and percents.

Option: Assign the **Extension** activity.

Partially Understanding the Mathematics

Students compare and order related fractions, such as halves, fourths, and eighths, or thirds and sixths. However, they are still developing strategies for comparing all fractions. They are able to use $\frac{1}{2}$ as a landmark and know which fractions are more or less than $\frac{1}{2}$. They don't always use their knowledge of fraction or percent equivalents to compare fractions. When students use diagrams, they may not always show the same-sized whole and equal pieces. They tend to rely entirely on the drawings, rather than on reasoning, which sometimes leads to inaccurate answers. Students correctly solve problems involving halves and fourths, but struggle to answer other problems.

Option: Assign the **Practice** activity.

Not Understanding the Mathematics

Because students are still developing an understanding of fractions, percents, and equivalents, they have a difficult time comparing and ordering fractions. They are just learning to use $\frac{1}{2}$ as a landmark and to consider the relationship between the numerator and denominator. When students use diagrams, they use wholes of different sizes, and may not show equal-sized parts, which leads them to incorrect answers. Students may be able to answer questions involving $\frac{1}{2}$, but struggle with other fractions or percents.

Option: Assign the **Intervention** activity.

Investigation 2 Quiz

In addition to your observations and students' work in Investigation 2, the Quiz (R31) can be used to gather more information.

Name _____ Date _____

What's That Portion?

Quiz

Choose the correct answer.

1. Which is the correct location for $\frac{4}{5}$?

   0% 10% 20% 30% 40% 50% 60% 70% 80% 90% 100%

   A. A   **B.** B   **C.** C   **D.** D

2. Which number is less than $\frac{1}{2}$?

   A. $33\frac{1}{3}\%$ **B.** $\frac{4}{5}$ **C.** 60%   **D.** $\frac{5}{8}$

3. Which fractions are written in order from least to greatest?

   A. $\frac{1}{3}, \frac{3}{4}, \frac{6}{10}$ **C.** $\frac{1}{3}, \frac{6}{10}, \frac{3}{4}$

   B. $\frac{3}{4}, \frac{6}{10}, \frac{1}{3}$ **D.** $\frac{6}{10}, \frac{1}{3}, \frac{3}{4}$

4. Which statement is true?

   A. $\frac{2}{5} < \frac{3}{10}$ **C.** $\frac{7}{8} < \frac{1}{6}$

   B. $\frac{2}{3} > \frac{1}{4}$ **D.** $\frac{9}{10} = \frac{3}{4}$

5. Janet ate $\frac{2}{3}$ of a can of chicken soup. Renaldo ate $\frac{1}{2}$ of a can of tomato soup. Renaldo says he ate more soup. Is that possible? Explain your thinking.

   Yes; explanations will vary. Review students' work.

Use after Session 2.6.   Unit 4 **R31**

Intervention

30 MIN   INDIVIDUALS

Equivalent Fractions
Use anytime after Session 2.1.

Math Focus Points

◆ Ordering fractions and justifying their order through reasoning about fraction equivalents and relationships

Vocabulary: equivalent fractions

Materials: colored pencils (at least 10 different colors), M10

Some students need additional support identifying equivalent fractions in order to work with fraction and percent equivalents.

Can you think of a fraction that is equivalent to $\frac{1}{2}$? How do you know?

Students might say:

"$\frac{5}{10}$ is equal to $\frac{1}{2}$. 5 is half of 10, so it's $\frac{1}{2}$."

"$\frac{2}{4}$ and $\frac{1}{2}$ are equal. I made a drawing to show that."

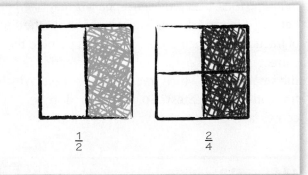

$\frac{1}{2}$ $\frac{2}{4}$

Give each student a copy of Fraction and Percent Equivalents (M10). Students will use this chart to identify equivalent fractions rather than equivalent percents. They will use different colors to circle sets of equivalent fractions.

Let's go column by column and circle all of the fractions equal to $\frac{1}{2}$. Use a colored pencil. Start by circling $\frac{1}{2}$ in the first column.

If students have difficulty, ask them to think about the numerator and denominator. For each column ask, Is there a fraction where the numerator is half the denominator?

After each equivalent fraction, students should write "= 50% = $\frac{1}{2}$."

What about $\frac{2}{2}$? Are there any other fractions equal to $\frac{2}{2}$? How do you know? Ask student to circle in blue all the fractions equal to $\frac{2}{2}$, including $\frac{2}{2}$. What does it mean when the numerator and denominator are the same? What percent would that be?

After each equivalent fraction, students should write "= 100% = 1."

Next, move to the fourths column. Ask students to fill in the percentages. If they need help, ask how many squares on the 10 × 10 grid would be colored in. Think about fourths and eighths. How many eighths is equivalent to $\frac{1}{4}$? How could you figure it out? Give students time to think about this; some might want to draw a representation. Once students have figured it out, have them write in the equivalents on the chart, "$\frac{2}{8}$ = 25% = $\frac{1}{4}$." Repeat this process for $\frac{6}{8}$.

 ELL English Language Learners

Provide a Word List Some students may still have difficulty with fraction names. Write the words *half, fourth,* and *eighth* on the board. Have students copy the words and then write the fraction and draw a picture for each.

Additional Resource
Student Math Handbook page 44

Practice

Ordering Fraction Cards

Use anytime after Session 2.3.

Math Focus Points

◆ Ordering fractions and justifying their order through reasoning about fraction equivalents and relationships

Materials: Fraction Cards (1 deck per pair), paper clips, R32

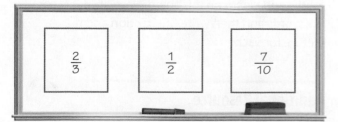

Materials to Prepare: Remove the percent cards from decks of Fraction Cards.

Today we're going to practice arranging fraction cards in order. Show the following on the board.

$$\frac{2}{3} \qquad \frac{1}{2} \qquad \frac{7}{10}$$

How would I arrange these fractions in order from least to greatest? How do you know?

Students might say:

"It would be $\frac{1}{2}$, then $\frac{2}{3}$, and then $\frac{7}{10}$. I can tell $\frac{1}{2}$ is the smallest. Then for $\frac{2}{3}$ and $\frac{7}{10}$, I thought about percents. $\frac{2}{3}$ is $66\frac{2}{3}\%$, and $\frac{7}{10}$ is 70%. So $\frac{7}{10}$ is the biggest."

Provide another example, such as $\frac{1}{4}$, $\frac{12}{10}$, and $\frac{3}{8}$. Then, give each pair a deck of prepared Fraction Cards and several paper clips.

Mix up the cards and draw three of them. Work with your partner to arrange the cards from least to greatest. If any of the fractions are equal, clip them together and draw another one. Arrange the cards in order, including the ones that are clipped together.

After you arrange five sets of fractions, mix them up again and try the same activity using four cards each time.

Distribute copies of Ordering Fraction Cards (R32).

ELL **English Language Learners**

Partner Talk Have pairs take turns explaining how the fractions are ordered. More proficient speakers should use words such as *equal, greater, greatest, less than,* and *least.* Less proficient speakers may need help explaining. Ask simple questions about the size of fractions and their order as students point to the correct fractions. For example: Which fraction is the smallest? So, which fraction comes first? Which fraction is the greatest? So, which fraction comes last?

Additional Resource

Student Math Handbook
Game: *In Between* SMH G10

Materials: Fraction Cards (diamond cards only)

Extension

20 MIN INDIVIDUALS

Finding Equal Amounts

Use anytime after Session 2.4.

Math Focus Points

◆ Finding and comparing fractional parts and percents of a whole or a group

Materials: R33

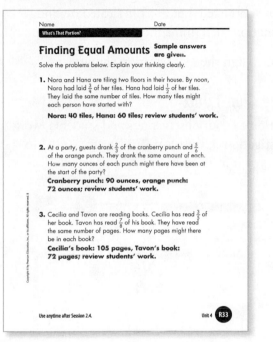

In this activity, students focus on equal amounts when fractions are not equal. Suppose half of the fourth graders and $\frac{2}{3}$ of the fifth graders ride the bus. In which class are there more students riding the bus?

Students might say:

"At first I thought there would be more fifth graders, but then I realized I need to know how many students are in each class. Then I can figure out which class has more students on the bus."

Suppose there are 26 fourth graders and 18 fifth graders. How many students in each class ride the bus? How did you figure it out? As students explain their thinking, record the results on the board.

Students might say:

"Half of 26 is 13. So 13 fourth graders ride the bus. For fifth grade, first I figured out a third of 18. I divided 18 by 3, and that's 6. So $\frac{2}{3}$ of 18 is 12."

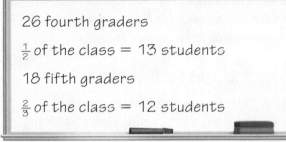

26 fourth graders

$\frac{1}{2}$ of the class = 13 students

18 fifth graders

$\frac{2}{3}$ of the class = 12 students

Try to figure out how many students there could be in each class so the same number of students are riding the bus. Discuss various solutions. Be sure students recognize that there is more than one solution.

Students might say:

"Change the fourth-grade class to 24. Half of 24 is 12. So now, 12 students in each class ride the bus."

Distribute copies of Finding Equal Amounts (R33).

ELL **English Language Learners**

Rephrase As students explain their thinking, pause and rephrase as necessary. Be sure students are not confusing the meaning of *fourth* as in *fourth-grade class* with *fourth* as used to describe a fraction.

Additional Resource

Student Math Handbook page 50–51

Differentiation in Investigation 3

Mathematics in This Investigation

The mathematics focuses on adding and subtracting fractions by using reasoning about fraction equivalents and relationships and by using different models of fractions, such as area, rotation, and number lines.

Additional Resource: *"We Didn't Do Math Like This in My Old School." Integrating a New Student,* pages 75–77 (See *Implementing Investigations in Grade 5*)

Understanding the Mathematics

Students correctly add and subtract fractions by using diagrams and by reasoning about fraction equivalents and relationships. They know some sums without calculating (e.g., $\frac{1}{2} + \frac{1}{4}$ or $\frac{1}{3} + \frac{1}{6}$). They use different models, such as a grid, clock, or number line, to help them add and subtract fractions. Students often break fractions into pieces to add or subtract, and are able to keep track of all the parts and get the correct answer. Students find correct sums and differences, know if their answer is reasonable, and clearly explain their reasoning.

Option: Assign the **Extension** activity.

Partially Understanding the Mathematics

Students correctly solve some fraction addition and subtraction problems, usually those with the same denominator or closely related denominators, such as halves and fourths or thirds and sixths. Students mostly rely on using grids or drawings to solve problems. While they may be able to solve problems using the clock or moving on the fraction tracks, they have difficulty understanding how that helps them to solve addition and subtraction problems. They are often unable to explain whether or not their answers are reasonable.

Option: Assign the **Practice** activity.

Not Understanding the Mathematics

Students are unable to add and subtract most fractions. They generally try to solve these problems in some way that is not based on the meaning of fractions. They might just add the numerators and add the denominators, and not realize that the result isn't reasonable. Students may draw correct representations of the fractions to be added or subtracted, but don't indicate how the representations determine the sum or difference.

Option: Assign the **Intervention** activity.

Investigation 3 Quiz

In addition to your observations and students' work in Investigation 3, the Quiz (R34) can be used to gather more information.

Name _____ Date _____

What's That Portion?

Quiz

Choose the correct answer.

1. Which numbers are written in order from least to greatest?

A. $1\frac{1}{2}, 1\frac{7}{8}, 1\frac{1}{4}$ **C.** $1\frac{7}{8}, 1\frac{1}{2}, 1\frac{1}{4}$

(B.) $1\frac{1}{4}, 1\frac{1}{2}, 1\frac{7}{8}$ **D.** $1\frac{1}{2}, 1\frac{1}{4}, 1\frac{7}{8}$

2. Which sum is greater than 1?

A. $\frac{1}{4} + \frac{1}{3}$ **C.** $\frac{1}{2} + \frac{1}{6}$

B. $\frac{5}{8} + \frac{1}{4}$ **(D.)** $\frac{7}{10} + \frac{2}{5}$

3. $\frac{5}{12} + \frac{1}{4} + \frac{1}{2} =$

A. $1\frac{1}{3}$ **(B.)** $1\frac{1}{6}$ **C.** $\frac{7}{12}$ **D.** $\frac{7}{18}$

4. $\frac{9}{10} - \frac{2}{5} =$

(A.) $\frac{1}{2}$ **B.** $\frac{7}{10}$ **C.** $1\frac{3}{10}$ **D.** $\frac{7}{5}$

5. Describe how to use a clock face to add $\frac{1}{6} + \frac{2}{3}$.

$\frac{5}{6}$; review students' work.

R34   Unit 4   Use after Session 3.10.

Intervention

30 MIN   INDIVIDUALS

Adding and Subtracting Fractional Parts

Use anytime after Session 3.3.

Math Focus Points

◆ Adding and subtracting fractions through reasoning about fraction equivalents and relationships

Vocabulary: lowest terms, equivalent fractions

Materials: colored overhead markers, colored pencils, M17, T49

This activity provides additional reinforcement of adding and subtracting fractions using rectangle models.

Give each student a copy of 4×6 Rectangles (M17) and display the transparency of the sheet (T49). Let's imagine that this first grid is a pan of brownies. My family ate $\frac{1}{6}$ of the pan on Saturday and $\frac{1}{2}$ of the pan on Sunday. How much of the pan did we eat those two days? Have students write $\frac{1}{6} + \frac{1}{2}$. How much of the grid should be shaded to show $\frac{1}{6}$? How much for $\frac{1}{2}$? How do you know? As students respond, use two different colors to shade the two portions of the grid on the transparency. Have students do the same.

Students might say:

"There are 24 brownies. 24 ÷ 6 = 4, so for $\frac{1}{6}$, shade 4 pieces. $\frac{1}{2}$ of 24 is 12, so shade 12 pieces for $\frac{1}{2}$."

How much of the grid is shaded? Is there an equivalent fraction for $\frac{16}{24}$? How do we see that in the grid? If students are unsure, divide the shaded grid vertically into thirds to illustrate that $\frac{16}{24} = \frac{2}{3}$. Students might also suggest $\frac{4}{6}$.

Next, have students write $\frac{5}{8} - \frac{1}{3}$ on their papers. Can you think of a story about brownies that fits this problem? After listening to students' stories, have students show the subtraction problem on another grid.

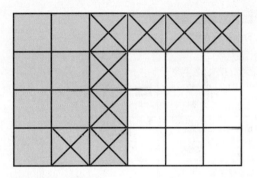

Have students use grids to solve the following problems. Provide extra copies of M17 as needed.

$\frac{3}{8} + \frac{1}{4}$ $\frac{1}{6} + \frac{2}{3}$ $\frac{5}{6} + \frac{1}{8}$

$\frac{1}{2} - \frac{1}{8}$ $\frac{7}{12} - \frac{1}{4}$

ELL   English Language Learners

Rephrase As students explain their reasoning, check to see that they relate *halves* to *dividing by 2*, *thirds* to *dividing by 3*, and so on.

Additional Resource

Student Math Handbook pages 52–53

Practice

Fraction Addition

Use anytime after Session 3.3.

Math Focus Points

◆ Adding and subtracting fractions through reasoning about fraction equivalents and relationships

Materials: M17 (as needed), M18 (as needed), M21 (as needed), R35

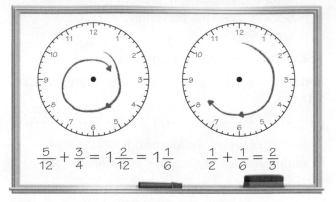

> Name _____ Date _____
> What's That Portion?
>
> **Fraction Addition**
>
> Find each sum. Then circle the sum that is closer to 1.
> In the space to the right of each problem, write how
> you decided which sum is closer to 1.
>
> 1. $\frac{1}{4} + \frac{7}{12} =$ ⑤/⑥   **Explanations will vary.**
> **Review students' work.**
>
> $\frac{2}{3} + \frac{1}{12} = \frac{3}{4}$
>
> 2. $\frac{3}{4} + \frac{2}{3} = 1\frac{5}{12}$
>
> $\frac{7}{12} + \frac{1}{2} = \boxed{1\frac{1}{12}}$
>
> 3. $\frac{1}{2} + \frac{3}{4} = 1\frac{1}{4}$
>
> $\frac{5}{6} + \frac{1}{12} = \boxed{\frac{11}{12}}$
>
> 4. Alicia bought $\frac{1}{4}$ yard of blue
>   ribbon and $\frac{2}{3}$ yard of purple
>   ribbon. Walter bought $\frac{1}{2}$ yard
>   of red ribbon and $\frac{5}{12}$ yard of
>   green ribbon. Who bought a
>   total amount of ribbon closer
>   to 1 yard? __**Walter**__
>
> Use anytime after Session 3.3.   Unit 4 **R35**

In this activity, students practice using various representations and strategies to help them add fractions and compare sums.

Mitch raked the yard for $\frac{5}{12}$ hour and washed the car for $\frac{3}{4}$ hour. Benito cleaned the family room for $\frac{1}{2}$ hour and sorted laundry for $\frac{1}{6}$ hour. Write the chores and times for each boy on the board.

Figure out how long each boy spent altogether on his chores. Then decide which boy spent closer to an hour doing his chores. Before you start, decide with your partner on a method you can both use to solve the problem. Then tell the rest of us what you did.

Students might say:

"We decided to use clocks. Mitch worked for $1\frac{1}{6}$ hours. Benito worked for $\frac{2}{3}$ hour. $1\frac{1}{6}$ hours is $\frac{1}{6}$ more than 1 hour, and $\frac{2}{3}$ hour is $\frac{1}{3}$ less. $\frac{1}{3}$ is greater than $\frac{1}{6}$. So Mitch was closer."

$$\frac{5}{12} + \frac{3}{4} = 1\frac{2}{12} = 1\frac{1}{6} \qquad \frac{1}{2} + \frac{1}{6} = \frac{2}{3}$$

Discuss other strategies. Present a similar problem and have pairs try a different representation or strategy to solve it such as $\frac{2}{3} + \frac{7}{12}$ and $\frac{3}{4} + \frac{5}{12}$.

Distribute copies of Fraction Addition (R35).

ELL **English Language Learners**

Model Thinking Aloud Some English Language Learners may have difficulty explaining their strategies. Model how to add fractions by drawing a picture as you share your thinking aloud. Draw a clock on the board. I want to add $\frac{5}{12}$ and $\frac{3}{4}$. I can draw a picture. There are 12 hours on the clock. Draw lines to show how the clock can be divided into 12 equal parts. So, $\frac{5}{12}$ can be shown by drawing an arrow through 5 parts—from the 12 to the 5. Draw the arrow. I know that $\frac{3}{4}$ is equal to $\frac{9}{12}$. So, I can draw another arrow through 9 parts—from the 5 to the 2. Together, the arrows show that $\frac{5}{12} + \frac{3}{4} = 1\frac{2}{12}$ or $1\frac{1}{6}$.

Additional Resource

Student Math Handbook
Game: *Roll Around the Clock* SMH G12–G13

Materials: fraction cubes ($\frac{1}{2}$ and less, $\frac{1}{2}$ and greater), Clock Fractions (*Student Activity Book* p. 37), M21

Extension

20 MIN | PAIRS

Adding Mixed Numbers

Use anytime after Session 3.1.

Math Focus Points

◆ Adding fractions by using a rotation model

Vocabulary: mixed numbers

Materials: M21, R36

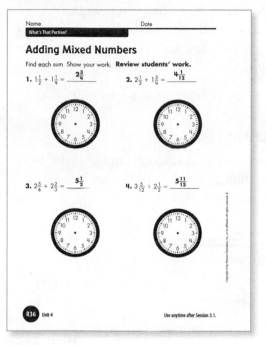

Write $1\frac{1}{6} + 2\frac{2}{3}$ on the board. If necessary, review the meaning of mixed numbers.

Give each student a copy of Large Clock Face (M21). Work with your partner. Use the clock face to add these mixed numbers. Then explain your solution.

Students might say:

"For $1\frac{1}{6}$, I made 1 full circle and then I went another $\frac{1}{6}$. For $2\frac{2}{3}$, I made another 2 full circles from where I left off and $\frac{2}{3}$ past that. So I went around 3 full circles and another $\frac{5}{6}$."

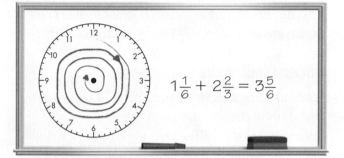

$$1\frac{1}{6} + 2\frac{2}{3} = 3\frac{5}{6}$$

"I used the clock to add the fractions $\frac{1}{6}$ and $\frac{2}{3}$ first. Then I added the whole numbers separately."

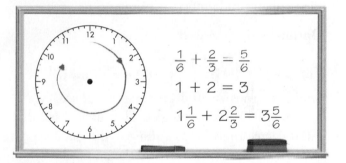

$$\frac{1}{6} + \frac{2}{3} = \frac{5}{6}$$
$$1 + 2 = 3$$
$$1\frac{1}{6} + 2\frac{2}{3} = 3\frac{5}{6}$$

Ask students to solve $2\frac{1}{4} + 3\frac{7}{12}$ using a different strategy and/or representation. Discuss student solutions. Then distribute copies of Adding Mixed Numbers (R36).

ELL ▸ **English Language Learners**

Provide a Word List Some students may not understand the meaning of a *mixed number*. Write *fraction* and *mixed number* on chart paper. Describe the difference and draw a picture to illustrate each. Then have students write examples.

Additional Resource

Student Math Handbook pages 52–53

Differentiation in Investigation 1

Mathematics in This Investigation

The mathematics focuses on describing and measuring angles by using known angles in the Power Polygon™ shapes to find the measure of other angles. There is also a focus on identifying attributes and properties of polygons.

Additional Resource: *Classification of Triangles and Quadrilaterals,* pages 137–138 (See Curriculum Unit 5)

Understanding the Mathematics

Students recognize 90-degree angles in polygons, regardless of the orientation of the figure. They understand that a 180-degree angle forms a straight line, and the angles around the center point of a circle total 360 degrees. They apply this information when they combine angles of the Power Polygon shapes to help them find angles that measure 30, 45, 60, 105, 120, and 150 degrees. Students understand the attributes and properties of various polygons.

Option: Assign the **Extension** activity.

Partially Understanding the Mathematics

Students recognize 90-degree angles, but usually only in squares and rectangles. They understand that a 180-degree angle forms a straight line, but don't necessarily use that idea to help them find the measures of other angles. Students typically use two or three of the same Power Polygon shapes to find other angles, rather than using different shapes. They find angles that measure 30, 45, 60, and 120 degrees. Students understand some of the attributes and properties of a limited number of polygons, such as squares and rectangles.

Option: Assign the **Practice** activity.

Not Understanding the Mathematics

Students have difficulty understanding what angles are and are sometimes unable to identify all the angles in a polygon. They might recognize 90-degree angles, but only in squares and rectangles. Students are unsure how to use one angle measure to find others, and they simply guess based on angle measures they have heard mentioned. They struggle to use Power Polygons to find actual angle measurements. Students have difficulty recognizing different polygons and understanding the attributes and properties associated with them.

Option: Assign the **Intervention** activity.

Investigation 1 Quiz

In addition to your observations and students' work in Investigation 1, the Quiz (R37) can be used to gather more information.

Name _____ Date _____

Measuring Polygons

Quiz

Choose the correct answer.

1. Which best describes the triangle?
   A. obtuse triangle   **C.** scalene triangle
   B. acute triangle   **D.** equilateral triangle

2. Which quadrilateral does **not** have 2 pairs of parallel sides?
   A. rectangle   **C.** trapezoid
   B. rhombus   **D.** parallelogram

3. If 3 equal angles are joined to make a right angle, what is the measure of each angle?
   A. 30 degrees   **B.** 45 degrees   **C.** 60 degrees   **D.** 90 degrees

4. Which best describes the polygon at the right?
   A. regular octagon   **C.** quadrilateral
   B. regular hexagon   **D.** decagon

5. Yumiko has 2 paper triangles. She marked an X on 2 angles that are the same size. She put the 2 angles together, and they filled the corner of a sheet of paper. What is the measure of each angle? Explain how you know.
   45°; review students' work.

Use after Session 1.7.   Unit 5 R37

Intervention

30 MIN   PAIRS

Making Angles

Use anytime after Session 1.5.

Math Focus Points

◆ Using known angles to find the measures of other angles

Vocabulary: right angle, acute angle

Materials: Power Polygons (4 of triangle E, 5 of triangle L per pair), R38

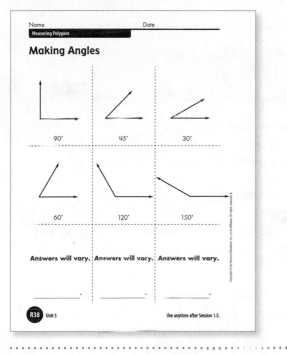

Give each student a copy of Making Angles (R38). Look at the 90° angle. What is another name for this angle? Ask students to examine the triangle E shapes. Have them identify the right angle and acute angles. How can you show that the two acute angles in triangle E are the same size?

Show students how to place two of the acute angles in triangle E to form a right angle.

Two of the acute angles fit exactly inside the right angle. So what is the measure of just *one* of the acute angles? How do you know? Have students trace around one acute angle of triangle E in the space labeled 45° on R38.

Using three triangle L shapes, help students arrange the three smallest angles inside the right angle. Again, ask them to determine the measure of just one of the angles. Have them trace around it in the space labeled 30°. If we used two of these 30-degree angles, what angle would that make? Have students put two 30° angles together and trace around them in the space labeled 60°.

Have pairs share their Power Polygons to make the 120° and 150° angles. For each angle, see if you can come up with a solution that is different from your partner's solution.

Students can continue to make angles of other sizes and record them in the third row of R38.

ELL English Language Learners

Use Repetition Question students as they develop the process for determining angle measures. How many angles fill the 90° angle? What should you divide to find the measure of one angle? What is the measure of one angle?

Additional Resource

Student Math Handbook page 99

Practice

20 MIN   PAIRS

Polygon Puzzles

Use anytime after Session 1.4.

Math Focus Points

◆ Identifying attributes of polygons

Materials: R39

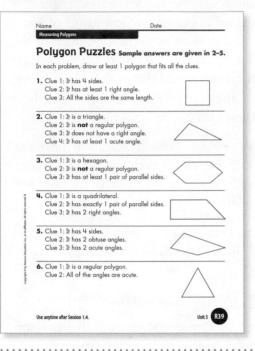

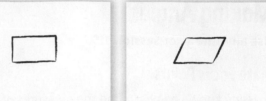

Present another puzzle.

> Clue 1: It is a quadrilateral.
>
> Clue 2: It is not a regular polygon.
>
> Clue 3: All the sides are the same length.

Draw a polygon that fits all three clues. Compare your answer to your partner's answer. Did you solve the puzzle the same way?

Students might say:

"We both drew a rhombus. Mine was pointier."

Ask each student to make up a 3-clue puzzle for his or her partner to solve. Then call on volunteers to share their puzzles with their classmates.

Distribute copies of Polygon Puzzles (R39).

Write the following clues on the board.

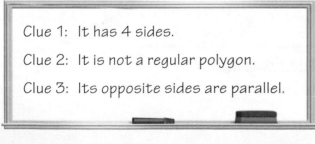

> Clue 1: It has 4 sides.
>
> Clue 2: It is not a regular polygon.
>
> Clue 3: Its opposite sides are parallel.

Draw a polygon that fits all three clues. Compare your answer to your partner's answer. Did you solve the puzzle the same way?

Students might say:

"I drew a rectangle and [Zachary] drew a different kind of parallelogram."

ELL   **English Language Learners**

Rephrase Read through each clue one at a time and rephrase as needed. For example, as you read Clue 2 in the first puzzle on the board, check to be sure students understand *regular polygon*. For Clue 3 in that same puzzle, check for understanding of the words *opposite* and *parallel*. Show examples as needed.

Additional Resource

Student Math Handbook pages 93–99

Extension

30 MIN | **GROUPS**

Angles in a Polygon
Use anytime after Session 1.5.

Math Focus Points
◆ Using known angles to find the measures of other angles

Materials: construction paper, ruler, scissors, tape

Draw and cut out a large triangle and number each angle. Then cut off each corner. Have each student do the same at their desks.

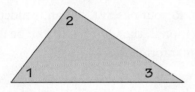

Draw a line on the board and demonstrate how to fit the angles together around a point on the line. Tape the pieces in place. Have students follow along with their own triangles.

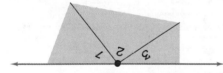

What do the three angles in my triangle add up to? Is that true in your triangle? What about the other triangles in your group?

Have students do a similar exploration for a quadrilateral. Remind students to label each angle so they can keep track of the vertices when they cut off the corners. Encourage group members to use a variety of quadrilaterals. What do the four angles in a quadrilateral add up to? Is that true for all the quadrilaterals in your group?

Next, have students explore pentagons. Observe how group members tackle the problem of the angles filling more than both sides of the line. Have one group demonstrate at the board while others follow along at their seats. Then ask students to figure out the sum of the angles.

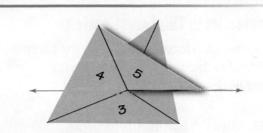

Students might say:

 "It's kind of like a spiral. We kept arranging the angles around a point like we did before. But when we added angles 4 and 5, they went on top of the other angles. We ended up at the line."

 "We went around $1\frac{1}{2}$ times in all. That's 360° for 1 time around, and then another 180° for the half time. So the angles add up to 540°."

Use the sum of the angles in a triangle, in a quadrilateral, and in a pentagon to predict the sum of the angles in a hexagon. Then make a large hexagon and see if your prediction was correct.

ELL **English Language Learners**

Provide a Word List Write the following words on the board: *angle, triangle, quadrilateral, pentagon, hexagon.* Review the meaning of each word. Some English Language Learners may already be familiar with the roots tri- and quad-. Have students copy the list and draw a picture to illustrate each word. Allow them to reference this list as needed.

Additional Resource

Student Math Handbook pages 99–101

Differentiation in Investigation 2

Mathematics in This Investigation

The mathematics focuses on finding the perimeter and area of rectangles, and examining the relationship between these two measures.

Understanding the Mathematics

Students have a clear understanding of perimeter and area as different types of measures. To create a rectangle with a given perimeter, students use the fact that the sum of the dimensions of a rectangle is $\frac{1}{2}$ of the perimeter (e.g., if the perimeter is 20, the dimensions add up to 10). To create a rectangle with a given area, students use pairs of factors of the area as the dimensions of the rectangle (e.g., if the area is 24, the two factors 4 and 6 could be the dimensions). Students understand that rectangles can have the same perimeter but different areas. They also understand that rectangles can have the same area but different perimeters. Students have little trouble finding dimensions for these related rectangles.

Option: Assign the **Extension** activity.

Partially Understanding the Mathematics

Students understand that perimeter and area are different types of measures, but they sometimes confuse the two. Students are still working on understanding what perimeter is, and they often need to label all four sides of the rectangle to help them keep track. When asked to make rectangles with given perimeters or areas, students often guess and check, and they rely on using square tiles or grid paper to find solutions. They are usually able to make rectangles that have the same area but different perimeters, but they struggle to make rectangles that have the same perimeter but different areas.

Option: Assign the **Practice** activity.

Not Understanding the Mathematics

Students have difficulty distinguishing between perimeter and area. They often are able to find the area of a rectangle, usually by building or drawing the rectangles and then counting the number of squares, but they struggle to find the perimeter of the same rectangle. If asked to build rectangles with given perimeters and areas, students guess and check, and they struggle to come up with even one example.

Option: Assign the **Intervention** activity.

Investigation 2 Quiz

In addition to your observations and students' work in Investigation 2, the Quiz (R40) can be used to gather more information.

Intervention

20 MIN   INDIVIDUALS

Making Rectangles

Use anytime after Session 2.4.

Math Focus Points

◆ Creating different rectangles with the same area but different perimeters

Vocabulary: perimeter, area

Materials: *Student Activity Book* p. 39, scissors, tape, M18

· ·

This activity offers a hands-on approach for students who need help visualizing the rectangles on *Student Activity Book* page 39.

Ask students to cut a rectangle 8 rows down and 3 tiles across on a sheet of Centimeter Grid Paper (M18). What is the perimeter? What is the area? Show me how you figured that out. Have students label their rectangle with a large 1. Then have them record the perimeter and area on *Student Activity Book* page 39, Problem 1.

Ask students to cut out another rectangle identical to the first. Provide extra grid paper as needed. Cut this new rectangle in half by cutting through the middle of the longer side. Slide the halves together to make a new rectangle with different dimensions from the first rectangle. Tape the pieces together and label your new rectangle with a large 2. What is the perimeter of the rectangle you made? What is the area? What do you notice about the area? Have students complete Problem 2.

Ask students to cut out another rectangle identical to the one labeled 2. Again, I want you to cut this new rectangle into two halves by cutting through the shorter sides. Tape the halves together to make a new rectangle with different dimensions from the first two rectangles. Label your new rectangle 3. Have students complete Problem 3.

Ask students to cut out another rectangle identical to the one labeled 3. Have them cut it in half through the shorter sides, and then tape the halves together to produce rectangle 4.

Have students line up the four rectangles in order.

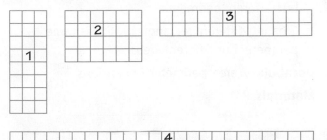

How are the shapes of the rectangles changing each time? How does this affect the area? How does this affect the perimeter?

Students might say:

"It looks like they're stretching out. They're getting thinner and thinner."

"The area never changes, but the perimeters of the longer rectangles are larger."

ELL) **English Language Learners**

Use Repetition To guide English Language Learners, repeat the following questions for each rectangle. What are the dimensions? What is the perimeter? What is the area? After each one, show students where to record the answer on page 39.

Additional Resource

Student Math Handbook page 102

Practice

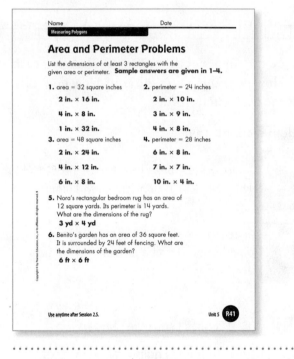

20 MIN   PAIRS

Area and Perimeter Problems

Use anytime after Session 2.5.

Math Focus Points

◆ Creating different rectangles with the same area but different perimeters

◆ Creating different rectangles with the same perimeter but different areas

Vocabulary: area, perimeter, dimensions

Materials: R41

Name _____ Date _____

Measuring Polygons

Area and Perimeter Problems

List the dimensions of at least 3 rectangles with the given area or perimeter. **Sample answers are given in 1–4.**

1. area = 32 square inches

  2 in. × 16 in.

  4 in. × 8 in.

  1 in. × 32 in.

2. perimeter = 24 inches

  2 in. × 10 in.

  3 in. × 9 in.

  4 in. × 8 in.

3. area = 48 square inches

  2 in. × 24 in.

  4 in. × 12 in.

  6 in. × 8 in.

4. perimeter = 28 inches

  6 in. × 8 in.

  7 in. × 7 in.

  10 in. × 4 in.

5. Nora's rectangular bedroom rug has an area of 12 square yards. Its perimeter is 14 yards. What are the dimensions of the rug?

  3 yd × 4 yd

6. Benito's garden has an area of 36 square feet. It is surrounded by 24 feet of fencing. What are the dimensions of the garden?

  6 ft × 6 ft

Use anytime after Session 2.5.   Unit 5 **R41**

Briefly review area and perimeter. Ask pairs to work together and give the dimensions of at least three rectangles with an area of 36 square feet. Record suggestions on the board. Then ask pairs to give the dimensions of at least three rectangles with a perimeter of 40 feet.

Area: 36 square ft	Perimeter: 40 ft
9 ft by 4 ft	10 ft by 10 ft
2 ft by 18 ft	8 ft by 12 ft
3 ft by 12 ft	5 ft by 15 ft
1 ft by 36 ft	2 ft by 18 ft
6 ft by 6 ft	

Is there a rectangle with an area of 36 square feet and a perimeter of 40 feet? Which one is it?

Let's look for another rectangle. This time the area is 24 square feet and the perimeter is 22 feet. Do you need to make lists like before to find the rectangle? What else could you do?

Students might say:

"My lists were shorter. I listed one pair of numbers with a product of 24. Then I checked the perimeter. If that didn't work, I tried another pair. When I got to 3 by 8, I stopped."

Distribute copies of Area and Perimeter Problems (R41).

ELL English Language Learners

Provide a Word List English Language Learners may easily confuse the words *area* and *perimeter*. Have students copy the words on a sheet of paper. Help students draw examples for each. Allow students to refer back to this list as needed.

Additional Resource

Student Math Handbook page 102

Extension

20 MIN   PAIRS

Cutting Up Rectangles

Use anytime after Session 2.4.

Math Focus Points

◆ Creating different rectangles with the same area but different perimeters

Materials: blank paper, R42

Name _____ Date _____

Measuring Polygons

Cutting Up Rectangles

Start with a 24-inch × 10-inch rectangle. Record its perimeter and area in the table. Imagine cutting through the middle of the longer side and rearranging the halves to make a new rectangle. Record the dimensions, perimeter, and area of the new rectangle in the table. Continue splitting the rectangle 5 more times. (Hint: If you are uncertain about how to split a fractional measure in half, look at a ruler.)

	Dimensions	Perimeter	Area
1.	24 in. by 10 in.	68 in.	240 sq. in.
2.	12 in. by 20 in.	64 in.	240 sq. in.
3.	6 in. by 40 in.	92 in.	240 sq. in.
4.	3 in. by 80 in.	166 in.	240 sq. in.
5.	$1\frac{1}{2}$ in. by 160 in.	323 in.	240 sq. in.
6.	$\frac{3}{4}$ in. by 320 in.	$641\frac{1}{2}$ in.	240 sq. in.
7.	$\frac{3}{8}$ in. by 640 in.	$1,280\frac{3}{4}$ in.	240 sq. in.

8. Look at your completed table. What are some things you notice?

Answers will vary. Review students' work.

R42   Unit 5   Use anytime after Session 2.4.

....

Students examine the area of related rectangles in which some of the dimensions include fractions. Draw a 16 × 5 rectangle on the board. Label the dimensions, then provide multiple sheets of paper and have students do the same. Let's suppose these are inches. Imagine cutting the rectangle in half by cutting through the middle of the longer side. Then picture making a new rectangle with the two halves. Have students sketch the new rectangle and record its dimensions, perimeter, and area.

Work with your partner. Split the rectangle six more times. For each new rectangle, record its dimensions, perimeter, and area.

When students are done, discuss the results. Ask students to explain how they worked with fractional units. Resolve any difficulties that may have arisen.

Dimensions (inches)	Perimeter (inches)	Area (square inches)
16 × 5	42	80
8 × 10	36	80
4 × 20	48	80
2 × 40	84	80
1 × 80	162	80
$\frac{1}{2}$ × 160	321	80
$\frac{1}{4}$ × 320	$640\frac{1}{2}$	80
$\frac{1}{8}$ × 640	$1,280\frac{1}{4}$	80

Suppose you keep making new rectangles until you get one that's almost as long and skinny as a line. What would its area be?

Students might say:

"Each rectangle had an area of 80 square inches. So, if you kept making new rectangles, the area would always be 80 square inches."

Distribute copies of Cutting Up Rectangles (R42).

ELL **English Language Learners**

Model Thinking Aloud To help English Language Learners understand the difference between perimeter and area, model your thinking aloud. Draw a 4 × 10 rectangle on the board. This is a 4 × 10 rectangle. Those are its *dimensions*. *Perimeter* is the distance *around* the rectangle. Trace around the perimeter with your finger. *Area* is the amount of space *inside* the rectangle. Point to the inside of the rectangle.

Additional Resource

Student Math Handbook page 102

Differentiation in Investigation 3

Mathematics in This Investigation

The mathematics focuses on creating and describing similar shapes. This includes examining the relationship among angles, side lengths, and areas of similar shapes.

Additional Resource: *Building Larger Similar Figures,* pages 153–154 (See Curriculum Unit 5)

Understanding the Mathematics

Students have little problem building similar shapes, and recognize that the angles are the same in similar figures. They also pay attention to the side lengths, realizing that to create a shape similar to another, all sides have to be increased (or decreased) by the same factor (e.g., all sides are 2 times as long, or all sides are $\frac{1}{2}$ as long). When building similar hexagons, students realize they have to use other shapes besides the hexagon. Students recognize the relationship between the increase in the side lengths and the area (e.g., if the sides are multiplied by 2, the area is multiplied by 4). They understand this is true regardless of the polygon.

Option: Assign the **Extension** activity.

Partially Understanding the Mathematics

Students are able to build similar shapes, particularly for shapes that can be made simply by replicating the same piece in the same orientation (e.g., rectangle). They have a more difficult time building similar shapes when they have to change the orientation of one of the shapes (e.g., triangle), or use different shapes (e.g., hexagon). Students understand the angles of the similar shapes are the same, but sometimes forget that all the sides have to be increased by the same factor. Students sometimes recognize that when the sides of a figure are doubled, they will need 4 times the number of smaller polygons to build it. However, they are not sure this will always be true.

Option: Assign the **Practice** activity.

Not Understanding the Mathematics

Students build some similar shapes, usually the rectangle and square, but struggle with other shapes. They have a limited understanding of similarity, being able to visually conclude shapes are similar, but not noticing they've increased each side by the same factor. When building similar shapes, students often only increase the length of one of the sides. They struggle to build similar hexagons, and they are uncertain how to find the area of the larger shapes.

Option: Assign the **Intervention** activity.

Investigation 3 Quiz

In addition to your observations and students' work in Investigation 3, the Quiz (R43) can be used to gather more information.

Name   Date
Measuring Polygons

Quiz

Choose the correct answer.

1. Which triangle is **not** similar to any of the others?

A.   **B.**   C.   D.

2. The area of a rectangle is 4 square units. In a similar rectangle, the sides are 3 times as long. Which is the area of the larger polygon?

A. 12 square units   C. 24 square units

B. 18 square units   **D.** 36 square units

3. Georgia made a trapezoid with 8 triangles. How many triangles would she have to use to make a trapezoid with sides 2 times as long?

A. 64   **B.** 32   C. 16   D. 10

4. Which measures are equal in every pair of similar polygons?

A. side lengths   **C.** angle measures

B. perimeters   D. areas

5. On a sheet of grid paper, draw 2 similar polygons so that one has sides that are 4 times as long as the other. Count squares to find the area of each.

Answers will vary. Review students' work.

Use after Session 3.5.   Unit 5 **R43**

Intervention

30 MIN | PAIRS

Making Similar Shapes

Use anytime after Session 3.3.

Math Focus Points

◆ Making a generalization about the change in areas of similar figures

◆ Building similar figures for polygons made from two or more Power Polygon pieces

Vocabulary: similar

Materials: color tiles, Power Polygons, ruler

....

This activity focuses on using Power Polygons to build simple similar shapes. Build the following trapezoid and show it to students.

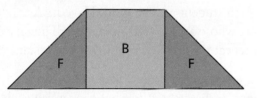

Build this trapezoid. Then work with your partner to build one with sides that are twice as long. Have students draw the original trapezoid and the larger one on paper. Have them use a ruler to make sure the larger trapezoid has sides twice as long as those of the smaller one. Some students might build their new shape using more B and F pieces. Others might notice that they can build it using pieces A and E. Be sure students understand that the two trapezoids are similar.

Suppose we measure the area of the trapezoids using piece B as 1 square unit. What is the area of the smaller trapezoid? How do you know?

Students might say:

 "The area is 2. There's one full B piece, and each triangle is half of a B piece. So that's 2 altogether."

What is the area of the larger trapezoid? If students are uncertain, have them fully cover their drawing of the larger trapezoid with piece B squares. Have them count each square inside the shape. Then help them count half squares along the slanted sides of the trapezoid.

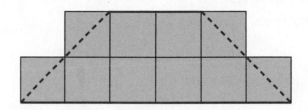

Next, have pairs build and draw a trapezoid with sides 3 times as long as in the original trapezoid. Let's use piece B again to measure the area of the biggest trapezoid.

When the sides doubled, what happened to the area? When the sides tripled, what happened to the area?

▬▬▬ **ELL** ▬▬▬ **English Language Learners**

Model Thinking Aloud To reinforce the meanings of the polygon names, use them in your explanations. For example: I made a *trapezoid* using two triangles and a square. Encourage students to use polygon names as they verbalize their own explanations.

▬▬▬▬▬▬▬

Additional Resource

Student Math Handbook pages 103–104

Practice

20 MIN   PAIRS

Drawing Similar Shapes

Use anytime after Session 3.2.

Math Focus Points

◆ Recognizing and building similar figures

Vocabulary: similar

Materials: colored pencils, M18, T13, R44

Name _____ Date _____

Measuring Polygons

Drawing Similar Shapes

1. On the grid, draw a shape with an area of 8 square units. Use whole squares only. Then draw 2 shapes similar to the original shape. One should have sides that are twice as long as the original shape. The other should have sides that are 3 times as long as the original shape.

Drawings will vary.

2. Find the area of each shape. Then explain how the areas compare.

The areas are 8 square units, 32 square units, and 72 square units. When the sides double, the area is multiplied by 4. When the sides triple, the area is multiplied by 9.

R44 Unit 5   Use anytime after Session 3.2.

Give each student a copy of Centimeter Grid Paper (M18). In one corner of the grid, draw a shape with an area of 6 square units. You may use colored pencils to color your shape, but use only whole squares. Then exchange papers with your partner. Draw two shapes similar to the shape your partner drew. The first should have sides that are twice as long as the original shape. The second should have sides that are three times as long as the original shape.

Ask volunteers to show their drawings on the transparency of Centimeter Grid Paper (T13).

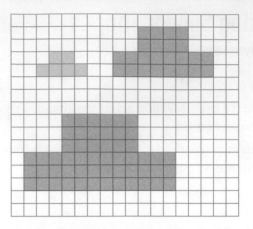

Your first shape has an area of 6 square units. When you doubled the sides, what happened to the area? When you tripled the sides, what happened to the area?

Give each student another grid. Have students draw a figure whose area is 10 square units. Then have them repeat the activity and share their results.

When each side of a shape is doubled, what happens to the area? What happens when each side is tripled?

Distribute copies of Drawing Similar Shapes (R44).

ELL English Language Learners

Provide a Word List Have students write *double*, *twice*, and *triple* on a sheet of paper. Explain that *double* and *twice* mean the same thing. They both mean *times 2*. *Triple* means *times 3*. Have students write these meanings on their papers.

Additional Resource

Student Math Handbook pages 103–104

30 MIN   GROUPS

Extension

Perimeter of Similar Figures

Use anytime after Session 3.3.

Math Focus Points

◆ Examining the relationship among angles, line lengths, and area of similar polygons

Materials: class chart from Session 3.3, M18 (as needed), Power Polygons (as needed), R45

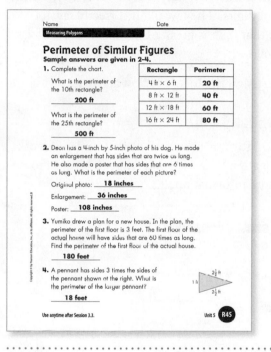

. . . .

Draw students' attention to the chart the class made during the discussion in Session 3.3. You saw a pattern in the way that area increases in similar polygons. Now you'll see if there's a pattern in the perimeters. Any predictions?

Students might say:

"I think it's going to change the same way that area changes."

"I don't think there's going to be a pattern. Or it might be different for different kinds of shapes."

Have students find the perimeter of a 4 × 6 rectangle. Then have them find the perimeter of rectangles that have sides that are 2, 3, 4, and 5 times as long. Record the results on the board.

Dimensions	Perimeter
4 units × 6 units	20 units
8 units × 12 units	40 units
12 units × 18 units	60 units
16 units × 24 units	80 units
20 units × 30 units	100 units

Ask students to generalize the results. What would be the perimeter of the tenth rectangle?

Let's see if your generalization holds true in other cases. Work in your groups. Each of you should use Centimeter Grid Paper (M18) or Power Polygons to create a non-rectangular polygon. Then make similar polygons by multiplying the lengths by 2, 3, 4, and 5. Compare the perimeters of the similar polygons. Is there a pattern? What is it? Did other group members reach the same conclusion?

Distribute copies of Perimeter of Similar Figures (R45).

ELL English Language Learners

Suggest a Sequence Some English Language Learners may benefit from a concise sequence of steps to follow, such as the following.

1. Draw a rectangular polygon.
2. Find the perimeter.
3. Draw similar polygons that are 2, 3, 4, and 5 times as long.
4. Find the perimeter of each.

Additional Resource

Student Math Handbook pages 103–104

Differentiation in Investigation 1

Mathematics in This Investigation

The mathematics focuses on using an understanding of fractions, the number system, and different models (e.g., grids and number lines) to compare and order decimals to the thousandths.

Additional Resource: *About Teaching Decimals, Fractions, and Percents Together,* pages 121–122 (See Curriculum Unit 6)

Understanding the Mathematics

Using hundredths grids, students correctly identify and shade in decimals to the thousandths place. They correctly write the decimal and fraction for equivalent numbers (e.g., 0.3, 0.30, 0.300). Students understand the relationship between tenths, hundredths, and thousandths (e.g., 1 tenth equals 10 hundredths). Students correctly place decimals on number lines. To compare fractions, students use fraction and percent equivalents, place-value concepts, and reasoning.

Option: Assign the **Extension** activity.

Partially Understanding the Mathematics

Students correctly identify tenths and hundredths on hundredths grids. They are still developing an understanding of the relationship of these decimals, so they have difficulty shading in thousandths. While students are beginning to understand decimals, they rely on shading in grids to compare decimals with a different number of digits (e.g., 0.3 and 0.25).

Option: Assign the **Practice** activity.

Not Understanding the Mathematics

Students count every square to identify hundredths on hundredths grids, but they struggle with tenths and thousandths. Students do not understand equivalent decimals, often seeing 0.1 and 0.10 as two different quantities. Because of their weak understanding of decimals, students usually treat them as if they were whole numbers. When trying to order decimals, they rely almost completely on the number of digits. They would incorrectly say, for example, that 0.25 is greater than 0.3 because 25 is more than 3.

Option: Assign the **Intervention** activity.

Investigation 1 Quiz

In addition to your observations and students' work in Investigation 1, the Quiz (R46) can be used to gather more information.

Name _____ Date _____

Decimals on Grids and Number Lines

Quiz

Choose the correct answer.

1. Which is the correct location for 1.75?

A. a   **B.** b   **C.** c   **D.** d

2. Which number does **not** describe the shaded part of the grid?

A. 0.375   **C.** 3.75
B. $\frac{375}{1,000}$ **D.** 37.5%

3. In 0.814, what does the 4 represent?

A. 4 ones   **C.** 4 hundredths
B. 4 thousandths   **D.** 4 tenths

4. Which numbers are shown from least to greatest?

A. 0.29, 0.4, 1.3, 0.06   **C.** 1.3, 0.4, 0.29, 0.06
B. 0.4, 0.06, 1.3, 0.29   **D.** 0.06, 0.29, 0.4, 1.3

5. Describe 2 different methods you can use to find a decimal equivalent to $\frac{1}{4}$.

Answers will vary. Review students' work.

R46   Unit 6   Use after Session 1.10.

Intervention

Ordering Decimals Through Hundredths

Use anytime after Session 1.3.

Math Focus Points

◆ Ordering decimals and justifying their order through reasoning about decimal representations, equivalents, and relationships

Vocabulary: decimal, tenths, hundredths

Materials: scissors; Decimal Cards, Set A (1 set per pair); M12; T63

Give each student a copy of Hundredths Grids (M12). Have them cut out each grid. Tell students to leave just a little plain paper beneath the grid, large enough to write a decimal.

Write the following decimals on the board.

| 0.35 | 0.7 | 0.65 | 0.5 |

Pick two decimals for yourself and the other two for your partner. Write each decimal under a grid and then shade the grid. Check each other's work. When students are done, discuss the results. Taking the decimals one at a time, ask a volunteer to show the shaded grid on the transparency of Hundredths Grids (T63). Draw special attention to 0.7. Why did [Olivia] shade 70 little squares instead of just 7?

Students might say:

"0.7 is 7 tenths. Each column of the grid is one tenth, so you have to shade 7 columns."

Now, spread out the four grids and arrange them from least to greatest. Check each pair's arrangement. Suppose you don't want to take the time to shade in the grids. Would you still be able to put the decimals in order?

Students might say:

"You could start with 0.5—that's $\frac{1}{2}$. 0.35 is less than $\frac{1}{2}$, and the other two are bigger."

Give each pair of students Decimal Cards, Set A. Have them remove 0, $\frac{1}{2}$, and 1 from the set, mix the cards, place them facedown, and select four of them to arrange in order. Tell students they can shade grids if they want to, but they should try to arrange the decimals by considering place-value clues and reasoning.

Have students mix the cards again, select five or six cards, and repeat the activity.

ELL English Language Learners

Partner Talk Show partners how to use the Decimal Cards to help them practice reading decimals. They can cover up the word form, take turns reading the decimal, and then check if what they said matches the word form. Have more proficient speakers read first. As less proficient speakers become more confident, have partners take turns going first. Make sure students use the words *tenths* and *hundredths* correctly.

Additional Resource

Student Math Handbook pages 55–56, 61–62

Practice

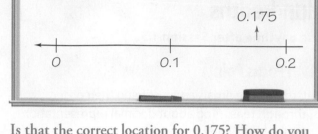

⏱ 20 MIN   👥 PAIRS

Decimals on a Number Line

Use anytime after Session 1.5.

Math Focus Points

◆ Ordering decimals and justifying their order through reasoning about decimal representations, equivalents, and relationships

Materials: Decimal Cards, Sets A and B; M12 (as needed); M17 (as needed); R47

Name _____ Date _____

Decimals on Grids and Number Lines

Decimals on a Number Line

Cecilia and her friends held a grasshopper jumping contest. The chart shows how far each person's grasshopper jumped. Use a letter to mark each distance on the number line. The first distance is done for you.

Grasshopper Jumping Contest	
Contestant	**Distance**
A. Cecilia	0.65 meter
B. Avery	0.3 meter
C. Walter	0.677 meter
D. Terrence	0.25 meter
E. Lourdes	0.5 meter
F. Janet	0.85 meter
G. Stuart	0.615 meter
H. Nora	0.79 meter
I. Felix	0.9 meter

Use anytime after Session 1.5.   Unit 6 **R47**

Is that the correct location for 0.175? How do you know?

Students might say:

"I was thinking of place value. The tenths place tells me 0.175 is somewhere between 0.1, and 0.2. The hundredths place tells me it's greater than 0.15. 0.15 is halfway between 0.1 and 0.2, so you have to put 0.175 past that."

Have students draw other cards and place the numbers on the number line. Have Hundredths Grids (M12) and Thousandths Grids (M17) available for students who wish to use them.

Distribute copies of Decimals on a Number Line (R47).

This activity gives students additional practice placing decimals less than 1 on a number line.

On the board, draw a large number line from 0 to 1 divided into tenths. Label 0 and 1. Ask a volunteer to write in the decimals.

Mix up a set of Decimal Cards, using both Sets A and B. Place the cards facedown. Ask a volunteer to pick a card and write the number on the number line.

ELL ▸ **English Language Learners**

Provide a Word List Have students write the words *tenths, hundredths,* and *thousandths* on a sheet of paper. Review the meaning of each word and help students write examples for each. Check that students can verbalize the word forms of decimals.

Additional Resource

Student Math Handbook
Game: *Decimals In Between* SMH G5
Materials: Decimal Cards, Set A; M13

Extension

30 MIN PAIRS

Repeating Decimals

Use anytime after Session 1.8.

Math Focus Points

◆ Interpreting fractions as division

Vocabulary: repeating decimal

Materials: *Student Activity Book* p. 35, calculators, R48

Name _____ Date _____

Decimals on Grids and Number Lines

Repeating Decimals

Find the first 3 decimal equivalents. Draw a bar to show which digit or digits repeat. What patterns do you see? Fill out the rest of the table using the pattern, then check your work.

1.

Fraction	Decimal
$\frac{1}{11}$	$0.\overline{09}$
$\frac{2}{11}$	$0.\overline{18}$
$\frac{3}{11}$	$0.\overline{27}$
$\frac{4}{11}$	$0.\overline{36}$
$\frac{5}{11}$	$0.\overline{45}$
$\frac{6}{11}$	$0.\overline{54}$
$\frac{7}{11}$	$0.\overline{63}$
$\frac{8}{11}$	$0.\overline{72}$
$\frac{9}{11}$	$0.\overline{81}$
$\frac{10}{11}$	$0.\overline{90}$

2. What pattern(s) did you notice and use to fill in the remainder of the table?
Answers will vary but should include something about skip counting or multiplying by 9. Review students' work.

3. Does the pattern you used for the chart work for $\frac{11}{11}$ and $\frac{12}{11}$? Explain why it does or doesn't work.
No; explanations will vary. Review students' work.

R48 Unit 6   Use anytime after Session 1.8.

Discuss some of the repeating decimals on *Student Activity Book* page 35, such as 0.333… and 0.1666…. Show students how to use a bar to show which digits repeat. Write $0.\overline{3}$ and $0.1\overline{6}$.

Let's think about ninths. Find the decimal equivalent for $\frac{1}{9}$ and $\frac{2}{9}$. Use the bar to show which digits repeat. Give students a minute or so to find the decimal equivalent, and check their work with a partner. List the equivalents on the board.

$0.\overline{1}$ $0.\overline{2}$

Ask students what the decimal equivalent for $\frac{1}{9}$ would be, reminding them if necessary that $\frac{1}{3}$ and $\frac{3}{9}$ are equivalent fractions. Talk with a partner. What pattern are you noticing? Give students a minute or two to discuss this with a partner.

Have students fill in the $\frac{1}{9}$ths row on *Student Activity Book* page 35. One of the things I'm curious about is why that pattern happens. Work with a partner, and use either a representation or a story context to see if you can come up with an explanation for why this pattern holds true. Give students around 10 minutes to work on this with a partner, and then discuss students' solutions. Remind students that as they explain, they should be able to connect the numbers to each part of their representation or story context.

Students might say:

"You want to do 1 divided by 9. But since we're working with decimals, we can't just divide the part into 9 pieces, we have to divide it into 10 pieces. You give 1 part to each of 9 people, then there's one part left. So you have to make that into 10 smaller parts. You give one smaller part to each of the 9 people, and there's one even smaller part left. You'd just keep doing that over and over."

Distribute copies of Repeating Decimals (R48).

ELL   English Language Learners

Rephrase Some English Language Learners may have difficulty with the word *equivalent*. Use other words or phrases that may be more familiar with students. For example, *equal* or *same value as* can be used in place of *equivalent*.

Additional Resource

Student Math Handbook page 60

Differentiation in Investigation 2

Mathematics in This Investigation

The mathematics focuses on adding decimals by reasoning about place value, equivalents, and representations.

Additional Resource: *Adding Decimals,* pages 132–133 (See Curriculum Unit 6)

Understanding the Mathematics

Students correctly add decimals by reasoning about place value and using what they know about addition. They understand they have to pay attention to the decimal point and the value of each digit when they add. They might use addition strategies they learned for whole numbers, such as adding by place or adding on the second number in parts. Students may also use decimal equivalents to add (e.g., writing all the numbers as thousandths.) Since students understand what decimals are, they're able to judge whether or not the sum they've found is reasonable.

Option: Assign the **Extension** activity.

Partially Understanding the Mathematics

Students correctly add decimals, mostly by shading in the decimals on hundredths grids and then combining them. They are beginning to use some reasoning about place value, but do not consistently pay attention to the place value of each digit. They may use reasoning to correctly add 0.5 and 0.35, but they have a more difficult time trying to reason about adding 0.375 and 0.05. As students keep adding decimal numbers, using reasoning or representations, they are beginning to get better at estimating whether or not their sum is reasonable.

Option: Assign the **Practice** activity.

Not Understanding the Mathematics

Using hundredths grids, students are able to add decimals that have the same number of digits (e.g., 0.5 + 0.3 or 0.45 + 0.25). When not using the grids, they usually treat decimals as whole numbers. They ignore the decimal point, add the numbers, and put a decimal point somewhere in the sum. Because they are still developing an understanding of what decimals represent, they have no idea whether or not their answers are reasonable.

Option: Assign the **Intervention** activity.

Investigation 2 Quiz

In addition to your observations and students' work in Investigation 2, the Quiz (R49) can be used to gather more information.

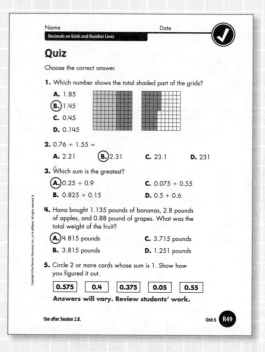

Intervention

30 MIN   PAIRS

Adding Decimals on Grids
Use anytime after Session 2.3.

Math Focus Points
◆ Using representations to add tenths, hundredths, and thousandths

Vocabulary: tenths, hundredths

Materials: Decimal Cards, Set A; colored pencils; T63; R50

Name _____ Date _____

Decimals on Grids and Number Lines

Adding Decimals on Grids

Answers will vary. Review students' work.

____ + ____ = ____

____ + ____ = ____

____ + ____ = ____

R50 Unit 6   Use anytime after Session 2.3.

Give each student a copy of Adding Decimals on Grids (R50). Begin with 0.45 + 0.7. Show students where to write this problem under the first pair of grids.

Shade the first grid to show 0.45. Then switch to another color. Continue from where you left off and shade another 0.7. When you fill the first grid, use the second grid.

When students are done, ask a volunteer to show the shaded grids. You may wish to use the transparency of Hundredths Grids (T63) turned sideways.

Ask students to explain how the shading for 0.45 was done. Then ask them to explain how the shading for 0.7 was done. Some students might think of 0.7 as 7 columns. Other students might think of 0.7 as 0.70: 70 little squares. How much is shaded in all? Have students write the sum on R50.

Give Decimal Cards, Set A to each pair of students. Have them remove 0, $\frac{1}{2}$, and 1 from the set, then have them mix up the cards and place them facedown. Ask each partner to pick a card. Students should work independently on R50 to find the sum of these two decimals. When they are done, ask partners to compare the results and try to resolve any discrepancies. Continue in this manner, providing extra copies of R50 as needed.

ELL English Language Learners

Model Thinking Aloud Write several decimals greater than 1 on the board. Model how to read each of the decimals being sure to emphasize the word *and* for the decimal point. As you read the decimal, move your finger across the decimal from left to right, pausing at the decimal point as you say *and*. For example: One *and* fifteen hundredths.

Additional Resource
Student Math Handbook pages 63–65

Practice

20 MIN   PAIRS

Decimal Addition

Use anytime after Session 2.6.

Math Focus Points

◆ Adding decimals to the thousandths through reasoning about place value, equivalents, and representations

Materials: Decimal Cards, Sets A and B; M12; M17; R51

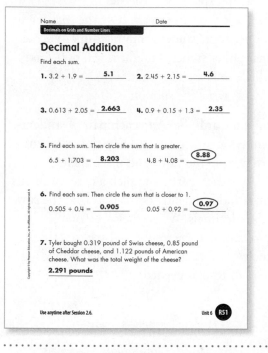

Name _____ Date _____

Decimals on Grids and Number Lines

Decimal Addition

Find each sum.

1. 3.2 + 1.9 = __5.1__   2. 2.45 + 2.15 = __4.6__

3. 0.613 + 2.05 = __2.663__   4. 0.9 + 0.15 + 1.3 = __2.35__

5. Find each sum. Then circle the sum that is greater.

   6.5 + 1.703 = __8.203__   4.8 + 4.08 = (8.88)

6. Find each sum. Then circle the sum that is closer to 1.

   0.505 + 0.4 = __0.905__   0.05 + 0.92 = (0.97)

7. Tyler bought 0.319 pound of Swiss cheese, 0.85 pound of Cheddar cheese, and 1.122 pounds of American cheese. What was the total weight of the cheese?

   2.291 pounds

Use anytime after Session 2.6.   Unit 6 R51

In this activity, students practice various strategies for adding decimals.

Last weekend, it rained 1.176 inches on Saturday and 0.81 inch on Sunday. Figure out the total rainfall for the weekend. When you are done, discuss your work with your partner. After pairs have shared their work, ask a volunteer to explain the strategies each partner used.

Students might say:

"I added the ones, then the tenths, then the hundredths, and then the thousandths. Then I put it all together. [Charles] wrote everything in thousandths and lined up the numbers like adding whole numbers."

$$1 + 0 = 1$$
$$0.1 + 0.8 = 0.9$$
$$0.07 + 0.01 = 0.08$$
$$0.006 + 0 = 0.006$$
$$1 + 0.9 + 0.8 + 0.006 = 1.986$$

$$\begin{array}{r} 1.176 \\ + \ 0.810 \\ \hline 1.986 \end{array}$$

Discuss other strategies. Then have pairs add 0.95 + 2.45. When students are finished, ask whether they used the same strategy they used earlier or switched to another strategy.

Students might say:

"For this problem, you can do it in your head. I took 5 hundredths from 2.45 and gave it to 0.95. Then all I had to add was 1 + 2.4 = 3.4."

Distribute copies of Decimal Addition (R51).

ELL   English Language Learners

Partner Talk Review the words *tenths, hundredths,* and *thousandths* with students. Have pairs explain their strategies. Beginning English Language Learners may only be able to say phrases like "I added" or complete the activity with a partner from their language group in their native language.

Additional Resource

Student Math Handbook
Game: *Close to 1* SMH G1
Materials: Decimal Cards, Sets A and B; M25

Extension

30 MIN PAIRS

Adding Many Decimals
Use anytime after Session 2.3.

Math Focus Points

◆ Adding decimals to the thousandths through reasoning about place value, equivalents, and representations

Materials: Decimal Cards, Sets A and B

In this activity, students add four, five, or six decimals.

Write $0.4 + 0.65 + 0.175 + 0.35 =$ _____ on the board. Solve this problem. Use clear notation so that your partner can understand what you did. Exchange papers and correct each other's work.

Give students time to complete these tasks. Then call on volunteers to explain their partner's work.

Students might say:

"[Margaret] circles all the ones and adds them. Then she circles the tenths and adds them. Then she adds the hundredths, and then the thousandths. Then she adds everything all up."

0̂.4 + 0̂.65 + 0̂.175 + 0̂.35	0
0.④ + 0.⑥5 + 0.①75 + 0.③5	1.4
0.4 + 0.6⑤ + 0.1⑦5 + 0.3⑤	0.17
0.4 + 0.65 + 0.17⑤ + 0.35	0.005
	1.575

Students might say:

"[Martin] says he usually writes the decimals up and down, and lines up the decimal point. But he said these numbers were easy to add mentally. $0.65 + 0.35 = 1$, and $0.175 + 0.4 = 0.575$. So the answer is 1.575."

Distribute Decimal Cards, Sets A and B to each pair of students or small groups. Have students play the game *Greatest Decimal Sum* as follows. For each round, mix the cards and place them facedown. Deal four cards to each player. Players work independently to add his or her four decimals. Each player checks another player's paper. The player with the greater (or greatest) sum gets a point. If there is a tie, no one gets a point.

Play two rounds with four cards per player. Then, play two rounds with five cards per player. Finally, play two rounds with six cards per player. The player with the greatest number of points after six rounds wins.

ELL **English Language Learners**

Provide a Word List Write the words *ones, tenths, hundredths,* and *thousandths* on the board. Provide a place-value chart and review the placement of each. As students discuss their work with one another, have them use the place-value chart to help them name the decimals.

Additional Resource

Student Math Handbook pages 64–65

Differentiation in Investigation 1

Mathematics in This Investigation

The mathematics focuses on reasoning about equivalent expressions in multiplication by doubling (or tripling) one factor and dividing the other by 2 (or 3). There is also a focus on using representations to support explanations.

Additional Resource: *Student Grouping that Enhances Learning,* pages 77–79 (See *Implementing Investigations in Grade 5*)

Understanding the Mathematics

Students use story contexts and representations to explain why doubling one factor and halving the other in a multiplication expression creates an equivalent expression. They may understand that doubling and halving always creates an equivalent expression, though one of the factors might be a fraction or decimal (e.g., $9 \times 15 = 4.5 \times 30$). They extend that reasoning to tripling one factor and dividing the other by 3. They create many equivalent expressions for 40×32, using relationships of the numbers. Through reasoning about the numbers and the operation, students are certain about whether or not multiplication expressions are equivalent.

Option: Assign the **Extension** activity.

Partially Understanding the Mathematics

Students are challenged to find a story context to help them understand why doubling one factor and halving the other in a multiplication expression creates an equivalent expression. Once they have the story context, drawing the representation helps them to better understand the idea. Students are not certain that tripling one factor and dividing the other by 3 results in an equivalent expression or are unsure what to do if one of the factors is not a whole number. When finding equivalent expressions for 40×32, they begin by thinking about doubling and halving, but they don't consider other relationships. Students solve the multiplication problems to be certain the expressions are equal.

Option: Assign the **Practice** activity.

Not Understanding the Mathematics

Students have a difficult time finding a story context and drawing a representation to help them understand why doubling one factor and halving the other in a multiplication expression creates an equivalent expression. The only way students are sure the multiplication expressions are equivalent is to solve the multiplication problems. Students find few equivalent expressions for 40×32.

Option: Assign the **Intervention** activity.

Investigation 1 Quiz

In addition to your observations and students' work in Investigation 1, the Quiz (R52) can be used to gather more information.

Name _____ **Date** _____ ✔

How Many People? How Many Teams?

Quiz

Choose the correct answer.

1. Which equation is illustrated by the diagram?
   A. $4 \times 9 = 9 \times 4$
   B. $4 \times 9 = 12 \times 3$
   C. $12 \times 4 = 8 \times 8$
   D. $12 \times 3 = 6 \times 6$

2. Which is the missing number?

   $20 \div 4 = 80 \div$ _____
   A. 16   B. 8   C. 5   D. 1

3. Which is **not** equivalent to 18×4?
   A. 3×24 B. 6×12 **C.** 9×2 D. 9×8

4. Last week, Mitch baked 48 muffins and packaged them in 8 bags with 6 muffins in each bag. This week, he baked twice as many muffins. How many bags does he need if he wants to package them the same way?
   A. 12 bags   C. 32 bags
   B. 16 bags   D. 96 bags

5. Use a story or a diagram to show why $5 \times 16 = 10 \times 8$.
   Answers will vary. Review students' work.

R52 Unit 7   Use after Session 1.4.

Intervention

30 MIN   PAIRS

Doubling and Halving

Use anytime after Session 1.1.

Math Focus Points

◆ Generating equivalent multiplication expressions by doubling (or tripling) one factor and dividing the other by 2 (or 3)

◆ Using story contexts and representations to support explanations of the relationship between equivalent expressions

Vocabulary: equivalent expressions

Materials: chart paper, centimeter cubes (60 per pair), index cards (10 per pair)

. . . .

Materials to Prepare: Write each story in the activity on chart paper.

Distribute cubes and index cards to each pair of students. Draw students' attention to the first story.

> A florist has 4 vases with 10 flowers in each vase. He noticed that 2 of the vases were leaking, so he threw them out. If he rearranges the flowers, how many will be in each vase?

Work with a partner. Arrange 4 index cards on your desk. Imagine that these are the 4 vases the florist started with. Put 10 cubes on each card to represent the 10 flowers in each vase. Each of you should draw a picture of your cards and cubes.

Now, you need to take away 2 of the vases because they leaked. First, divide up the flowers that are in those vases and put them in the other 2 vases. There have to be the same number of flowers in each vase. Then take away the leaky vases. Draw a picture to show what the cards and cubes look like now. How many flowers are in each vase now?

Ask a volunteer to share his or her pictures on the board. Ask another volunteer to write a multiplication expression for each situation.

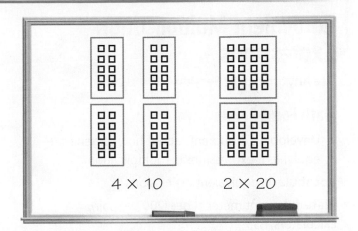

4×10 2×20

How do we know 4×10 and 2×20 have the same product? Students might multiply and say they know $40 = 40$. Remind them about the problem they just solved and that they didn't add or take away any flowers, so the products are equal. Remind students this can be called doubling and halving.

Repeat the activity using the next story.

> When Shandra moved her computer store to a new location, she packed up 6 boxes with 4 laptop computers in each box. The boxes weren't very full, so she decided to use 3 boxes, instead. How many laptops will be in each box?

Finally, have pairs work together to show that $8 \times 7 = 4 \times 14$. They should make up a story, represent it with cards and cubes, and draw a picture for each expression.

ELL) **English Language Learners**

Rephrase Story problems are especially difficult for English Language Learners. Before each story, discuss unfamiliar words (e.g., vase, laptop). Then, rephrase stories to eliminate extra information.

Additional Resource

Student Math Handbook pages 33–34

Practice

25 MIN **PAIRS**

Equivalent Multiplication Expressions

Use anytime after Session 1.3.

Math Focus Points

◆ Developing arguments about how to generate equivalent expressions in multiplication

Vocabulary: equivalent expressions

Materials: centimeter cubes (200 per pair), calculators, R53

Students might say:

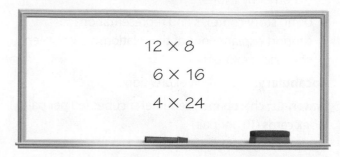

"I made 6 groups with 16 cubes in a group. Cecilia made 4 groups with 24 cubes in a group. We both still had 96 cubes."

Write the following on the board.

> 12×8
>
> 6×16
>
> 4×24

If you start with 12×8, what can you do to those factors to get 6×16? If you start with 12×8, what can you do to those factors to get 4×24? Are there any other equivalent expressions? As students offer suggestions, add them to the list on the board.

Write 36×50 on the board. Have students work independently to generate at least five equivalent expressions. Then have partners compare answers. For any expression that is not on both papers, have the student who created it explain to his or her partner what was done to the original factors to create the new ones.

Distribute copies of Equivalent Multiplication Expressions (R53).

Write 12×8 on the board. I want each of you to make 12 groups of cubes with 8 cubes in each group. How many cubes are there in all? I want one partner to rearrange the cubes so you have half as many groups. I want the other partner to rearrange the cubes so there are a third of the number of groups. How many cubes are there in your new arrangement? Give students time to complete the task and then ask them to describe the results.

 ELL **English Language Learners**

Model Thinking Aloud Help students verbalize the steps they used to generate an equivalent expression. For example: I used the first factor and divided it by 2. Then, I used the second factor and I multiplied it by 2. This made an equivalent expression.

Additional Resource

Student Math Handbook pages 33–34

Extension

🕐 20 MIN 👥 PAIRS

More Equivalent Multiplication Expressions

Use anytime after Session 1.3.

Math Focus Points

◆ Developing an argument about how to generate equivalent expressions in multiplication

◆ Using story contexts and representations to support explanations of the relationship between equivalent expressions

Materials: calculators, R54

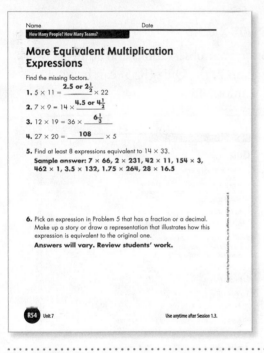

Students extend their work with equivalent multiplication expressions to include fractions and decimals. Write 4 × 25 on the board. **Work with your partner and write at least five equivalent expressions.** Students might need a hint that it's okay to use fractions or decimals. Record suggestions on the board.

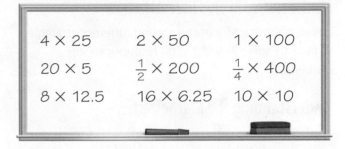

4 × 25	2 × 50	1 × 100
20 × 5	$\frac{1}{2}$ × 200	$\frac{1}{4}$ × 400
8 × 12.5	16 × 6.25	10 × 10

How do you know these expressions are all equivalent?

Students might say:

"They're all equal to 100. We checked some of them on the calculator."

"They're all made the same way. You multiply one factor by a number and divide the other factor by the same number. It's like when we were finding different rectangles with the same area."

Pick an expression with a fraction or a decimal. Make up a story that illustrates how this expression is equivalent to the original one.

Distribute copies of More Equivalent Multiplication Expressions (R54).

ELL **English Language Learners**

Provide a Word List Write the words *equivalent, expression, factor, fraction,* and *decimal* on chart paper. Review the meaning of each with students. Then have them work together to write examples next to each word. Post the list in the classroom for reference.

Additional Resource

Student Math Handbook pages 33–34

Unit 7

Differentiation in Investigation 2

Mathematics in This Investigation

The mathematics focuses on using different strategies to fluently solve 2- and 3-digit multiplication problems.

Understanding the Mathematics

Students have a strong understanding of the operation of multiplication and are able to solve problems fluently. Students keep track of what parts of the problem they have solved and what remains to be solved. They are able to solve a multiplication problem when given a first step. Students begin using different strategies to solve multiplication problems, based on the numbers given in the problem. Students realize they can use the same strategies to multiply 3-digit numbers that they used to multiply 2-digit numbers.

Option: Assign the **Extension** activity.

Partially Understanding the Mathematics

Students understand the operation of multiplication, but they are working at becoming efficient and accurate. They are working mostly numerically but will use representations to help them keep track of their work. Students are beginning to break the numbers into fewer parts (e.g., breaking 45 into 20 + 20 + 5), but they are still not using the biggest reasonable chunks. They are likely to have trouble keeping track of what parts of the problem they have solved and what remains. They often struggle in solving a multiplication problem when given the first step. When multiplying 2-digit by 3-digit numbers, students are more prone to error because they are breaking the numbers into so many parts.

Option: Assign the **Practice** activity.

Not Understanding the Mathematics

Students are still developing an understanding of the operation of multiplication. They are unable to solve most 2-digit multiplication problems because they don't find all the partial products, or they multiply incorrectly. While students are beginning to multiply by 10s, they often make mistakes. These students often do not think about, or see, the relationships between numbers when solving problems (e.g., how knowing $5 \times 8 = 40$ helps them to know $5 \times 80 = 400$).

Option: Assign the **Intervention** activity.

Investigation 2 Quiz

In addition to your observations and students' work in Investigation 2, the Quiz (R55) can be used to gather more information.

Name _____ Date _____

How Many People? How May Teams?

Quiz

Choose the correct answer.

1. Georgia multiplied 37 × 53 as shown at the right. What part of the problem does 350 represent?

   A. 30 × 50   **C.** 7 × 5
   B. 7 × 50   **D.** 70 × 50

   37
   × 53
   ‾‾‾
   21
   90
   350
   + 1,500
   ‾‾‾‾‾
   1,961

2. Alex multiplied 45 × 28 as shown at the right. What part of the problem does 900 represent?

   A. 40 × 20   **C.** 45 × 20
   B. 45 × 2   **D.** 45 × 8

   1
   4
   45
   × 28
   ‾‾‾
   360
   + 900
   ‾‾‾‾‾
   1,260

3. 68 × 34 =

   A. 476   **B.** 2,172   **C.** 2,212   **D.** 2,312

4. A grocer ordered 142 cases of juice. There are 24 cans of juice in each case. How many cans did the grocer order in all?

   A. 4,408 cans   **C.** 3,308 cans
   B. 3,408 cans   **D.** 852 cans

5. Estimate the product 375 × 22. Show how you made your estimate.

   Answers will vary. Review students' work.

Use after Session 2.4.   Unit 7 R55

Intervention

20 MIN   INDIVIDUALS

Partial Products

Use anytime after Session 2.2.

Math Focus Point

◆ Solving 2-digit by 2-digit or 3-digit multiplication problems fluently

Vocabulary: partial products

This activity focuses on keeping track of partial products when solving a multiplication problem.

Write 27 × 34 on the board. Then draw the following array, but do not label the inside of the boxes. Review how to break apart a 2-digit number into tens and ones so that students understand the labels along the sides of the array. Then ask students to help you label the inside of each box as you discuss what each box means.

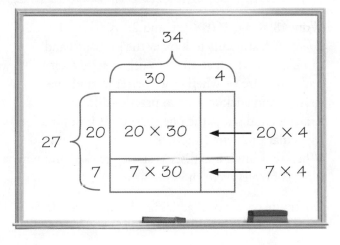

If we use this array as a guide, which products do we have to figure out in order to solve 27 × 34? Label each box as students call out each expression. These are the partial products of the problem. Ask students to calculate the four partial products and find their sum. Ask volunteers to show their work on the board.

Some of you have another very organized way of recording your work. It helps you keep track of all the partial products that are shown in the array.

$$
\begin{array}{r}
27 \\
\times\ 34 \\
\hline
28 \quad \leftarrow 7 \times 4 \\
80 \quad \leftarrow 20 \times 4 \\
210 \quad \leftarrow 7 \times 30 \\
+\ 600 \quad \leftarrow 20 \times 30 \\
\hline
918
\end{array}
$$

You can find the partial products in any order, but it helps if you get in the habit of always doing it the same way. Multiply both parts of 27 by 4, and then multiply both parts of 27 by 30.

Have students solve 45 × 28. They may draw an array if they are uncertain about how to generate the partial products. Remind students that each part of one factor must be multiplied by each part of the other factor and then added together. Have them check that they have included all of the partial products.

ELL **English Language Learners**

Provide a Word List Write the words *ones*, *tens*, and *partial product* on the board. Review the meaning of each. Emphasize that a *partial product* is *part* of a product. Then have students write the words on a sheet of paper and write an example for each. Allow them to reference this list as needed.

Additional Resource

Student Math Handbook page 30

Practice

Practicing Multiplication

Use anytime after Session 2.2.

Math Focus Points

◆ Solving 2-digit by 2-digit or 3-digit multiplication problems fluently

Vocabulary: partial products

Materials: R56

Name _____ Date _____

How Many People? How May Teams?

Practicing Multiplication

Solve the problems. Show your work clearly.
Review students' work.

1. 32 × 46 = __1,472__   2. 24 × 40 = __960__

3. 112 × 37 = __4,144__   4. 19 × 84 = __1,596__

5. 106 × 31 = __3,286__   6. 227 × 53 = __12,031__

In this activity, students continue to practice, refine, and share strategies for multiplying 2-digit numbers by 2-digit and 3-digit numbers.

Write 124 × 39 on the board. Solve this problem, and then compare your solution with your partner. Whose solution do you like better? Ask volunteers to present what they judge to be the better of the pair's two strategies.

Students might say:

"I like the way [Hana] did it. She did 124 times 40. She multiplied 124 by 20 two times. She added it all up, and then subtracted the extra 124."

$$124 × 20 = 2,480 \qquad 4,960$$
$$124 × 20 = \underline{2,480} \qquad - \;\; 124$$
$$\qquad\qquad 4,960 \qquad 4,836$$

Students might say:

"I broke apart 124 into 100 + 20 + 4. Then I multiplied each part by 39."

$$100 × 39 = 3,900$$
$$20 × 39 = 780$$
$$4 × 39 = 156$$
$$3,900 + 780 + 156 = 4,836$$

Write 48 × 34, 160 × 25, and 28 × 65 on the board. Ask students to look at the problems and think about which strategy to use to solve each problem. Discuss whether it's better to find one strategy and stick to it or to practice different strategies and select the one that seems best for a particular problem. Students solve the problems. When they are done, discuss strategies used and why those strategies were chosen.

Distribute copies of Practicing Multiplication (R56).

English Language Learners

Partner Talk Pair ELLs to give them practice with English. Have them explain their strategies. Beginning English Language Learners may only be able to respond using short phrases like "same as" or "small parts." Encourage more proficient speakers to use words like *equivalent, break apart,* and *partial products.*

Additional Resource

Student Math Handbook pages 30–32

Extension

20 MIN   PAIRS

Practicing Multiplication Strategies

Use anytime after Session 2.1.

Math Focus Points

◆ Solving 2-digit by 2-digit or 3-digit multiplication problems fluently

◆ Describing and comparing strategies used to solve multidigit multiplication problems

Materials: R57

Name _____ Date _____
How Many People? How May Teams?

Practicing Multiplication Strategies

Solve each multiplication problem by writing an equivalent problem. **Review students' work.**

1. $84 \times 15 =$ ___**1,260**___   2. $418 \times 50 =$ ___**20,900**___

Solve each multiplication problem by changing one factor and then making an adjustment.

3. $215 \times 29 =$ ___**6,235**___   4. $121 \times 52 =$ ___**6,292**___

Solve each multiplication problem. Use any strategy.

5. $120 \times 31 =$ ___**3,720**___   6. $888 \times 25 =$ ___**22,200**___

7. $22 \times 35 =$ ___**770**___   8. $311 \times 49 =$ ___**15,239**___

Use anytime after Session 2.1.   Unit 7   R57

....

This activity focuses on strategies that simplify the process of solving some multiplication problems.

Write 112×28 on the board. One partner should solve this problem using an equivalent problem. The other partner should solve the problem by changing just one factor and then making an adjustment to find the final answer.

Ask partners to explain their solutions to one another. Then call on volunteers to explain their partner's work to their other classmates.

Students might say:

"[Lourdes] made an equivalent problem. She multiplied 112 by 4 and divided 28 by 4, and she got 448×7."

"[Alex] changed the problem to 112×30. He multiplied 112×30 and had to subtract 224."

Have a discussion about whether one of these strategies seems easier and why. There is no "right" answer. Students should be able to explain why they prefer a strategy and to try other strategies as well. Have partners switch strategies and solve 230×48. Ask volunteers to explain their partner's work.

Distribute copies of Practicing Multiplication Strategies (R57).

ELL **English Language Learners**

Provide Sentence Stems Provide a format to help students explain their work. For example: For one factor, I would _____ (multiply by 4). For the other factor, I would _____ (divide by 4). Then, I would _____ (multiply 28 by 100 to get 2,800). This gives the product of 112×25.

Additional Resource

Student Math Handbook pages 31–32

Differentiation in Investigation 3

Mathematics in This Investigation

The mathematics focuses on efficiently solving division problems with 2-digit divisors.

Additional Resource: *Division Strategies*, page 125 (See Curriculum Unit 7)

Understanding the Mathematics

Students solve division problems efficiently by using either multiplication or division, using the biggest reasonable "chunks" of numbers. They keep track of all parts of the problem and use clear and concise notation in their answers. Students understand how knowing groups of multiples of 10 helps them solve division problems more efficiently. They are beginning to consider other strategies to solve division problems.

Option: Assign the **Extension** activity.

Partially Understanding the Mathematics

Students understand what the operation of division is, and they solve division problems correctly, but they need to improve their efficiency. They understand and use the relationship between multiplication and division. They may break the numbers into too many parts and struggle to keep track of all of their work. They are more comfortable working with the 10th or 20th multiple when solving division problems but are still using too many steps, which often leads to computational errors.

Option: Assign the **Practice** activity.

Not Understanding the Mathematics

Students are likely to understand what the operation of division is, but they are not efficient in using division strategies. When solving division problems, they are beginning to use multiples of the divisor but are not comfortable working with the 10th multiple. As students work through the problem, they have difficulty keeping track of the work and knowing what the answer is. They may get the correct answer, but their work is very time consuming.

Option: Assign the **Intervention** activity.

Investigation 3 Quiz

In addition to your observations and students' work in Investigation 3, the Quiz (R58) can be used to gather more information.

Name _____ Date _____

Decimals on Grids and Number Lines

Quiz

Choose the correct answer.

1. Which notation can **not** be used to mean how many groups of 16 are in 336?
   A. $16\overline{)336}$
   C. 16×336
   B. $336 \div 16$
   D. $\frac{336}{16}$

2. The answer to $514 \div 35$ is
   A. 14 R24   B. 14 R14   C. 13 R59   D. 11 R16

3. The answer to $1,200 \div 44$ is
   A. 27 R12   B. 27 R22   C. 29 R24   D. 117 R12

4. A florist has 640 roses. She is making bouquets with 12 roses in each bouquet. How many full bouquets can she make?
   A. 52 bouquets   C. 54 bouquets
   B. 53 bouquets   D. 63 bouquets

5. Mitch divided 2,650 by 25. His first step is shown below. Show how to complete the problem.

   $2,500 \div 25 = 100$

   106; review students' work.

R58   Unit 7   Use after Session 3.7.

Intervention

25 MIN INDIVIDUALS

Using Multiples to Divide

Use anytime after Session 3.3.

Math Focus Point

◆ Solving division problems with a 2-digit divisor fluently

◆ Using clear and concise notation

Vocabulary: multiple

....

This activity focuses on using multiples to help students decide how to start a division problem.

Mrs. Stein's gym class is counting by 16s. Each student says one number. The last student says 512. How many students counted? Ask students to state a division problem to represent this story.

When you start a division problem, it helps to think about multiples of the divisor. What are the first five multiples of 16? As students respond, write the multiples on the board.

Those numbers aren't close to 512, but we can use them to find larger multiples. What is the 10th multiple of 16? The 20th? The 30th? The 40th? The 50th? How can you easily find those from the first list of smaller multiples? Record the multiples as students respond.

1 × 16 = 16	10 × 16 = 160
2 × 16 = 32	20 × 16 = 320
3 × 16 = 48	30 × 16 = 480
4 × 16 = 64	40 × 16 = 640
5 × 16 = 80	50 × 16 = 800

Could you use any of the larger multiples for your first step?

Students might say:

 "I could use the 10th multiple. I could keep doing chunks of 160 until I get close to 512."

 "I'd pick the 30th multiple. 480 is a lot closer without being too big."

Start with one of the larger multiples and record the first step on your paper. 480 is a good place to start if you want to cut down on the number of steps. What do you still have to solve after your first step? How do you know? Do any of the multiples we've listed help out?

Have students complete the division problem and discuss their solutions. Model this notation for them, asking students what each of the numbers show.

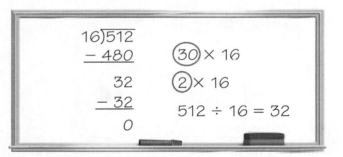

Repeat this process for 945 ÷ 27.

ELL) **English Language Learners**

Use Repetition Help students explain their solution by asking short, direct questions about each step such as:

◆ What division problem are you solving?

◆ What multiple did you use?

◆ How did that help you solve the problem?

◆ What did you do next?

Additional Resource

Student Math Handbook pages 38–39

Practice

Practicing Division

Use anytime after Session 3.3.

Math Focus Points

◆ Solving division problems with a 2-digit divisor fluently

Materials: R59

In this activity, students use number sense to help them refine strategies for solving division problems.

Write 742 ÷ 14 on the board. Before you solve this problem, I want to show you three different ways I've seen some of you start a problem like this. Write the following on the board.

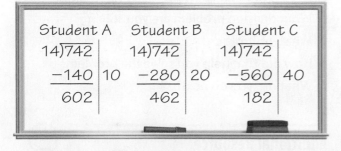

Student A		Student B		Student C	
14)742		14)742		14)742	
−140	10	−280	20	−560	40
602		462		182	

How are these first steps related? Do you like one better than the other? Why?

Students might say:

"Student A started with just 10 groups of the 14. Student B used 20 groups, and Student C used 40 groups. I'd do it like Student C because there won't be as many steps."

You know that 140 ÷ 14 = 10, but 140 isn't very close to 742. 20 groups would only get you to 280. So try 30 groups or 40 groups. Have students help you summarize this on the board.

10 groups:	140 ÷ 14 = 10
20 groups:	280 ÷ 14 = 20
30 groups:	420 ÷ 14 = 30
40 groups:	560 ÷ 14 = 40

Have students complete the solution for 742 ÷ 14.

Distribute copies of Practicing Division (R59).

ELL   English Language Learners

Use Repetition Have students explain their solution to you. Ask short simple questions, such as:

◆ What is your first step?
◆ What do you have left to solve?
◆ Then what did you do?
◆ Now, what do you have left to solve?

Additional Resource

Student Math Handbook pages 38–39

Extension

20 MIN GROUPS

Practicing Division Strategies
Use anytime after Session 3.2.

Math Focus Points
◆ Solving division problems with a 2-digit divisor fluently

Materials: R60

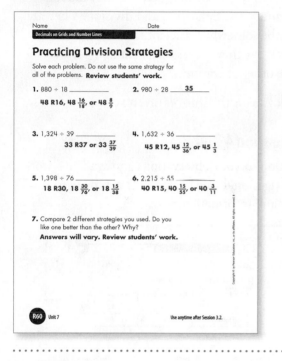

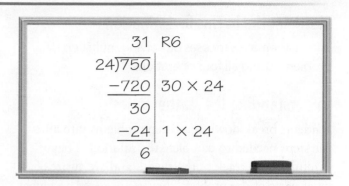

$$31 \; R6$$
$$24\overline{)750}$$
$$-720 \mid 30 \times 24$$
$$30$$
$$-24 \mid 1 \times 24$$
$$6$$

Students might say:

"I made an equivalent problem by dividing both numbers by 2, so I solved 375 divided by 12. I got a little confused with the remainder so I used a fraction."

$$750 \div 24 = 375 \div 12$$
$$360 \div 12 = 30$$
$$15 \div 12 = 1\frac{1}{4}$$
$$\left(375 \div 12 = 31\frac{1}{4}\right)$$

In this activity, students compare various strategies for solving division problems.

Have students solve $750 \div 24$. When students are finished, ask volunteers who use different strategies to present their solutions.

Students might say:

"I know $3 \times 24 = 72$, so $30 \times 24 = 720$. Then I subtracted 720 from 750 and made 1 more group. I wrote 31 R6 at the top."

Are both answers correct? Now solve $2,552 \div 48$ by making an equivalent problem. Think about what to do with any leftovers.

Students should divide both numbers by 2 or 4. When students are finished, discuss solutions, including what to do with the leftovers.

Distribute copies of Practicing Division Strategies (R60).

ELL English Language Learners

Suggest a Sequence Provide a sequence of steps for English Language Learners to follow. For example: *First,* find an equivalent problem. *Then,* divide to solve the problem. *Last,* write the answer using a fraction.

Additional Resource

Student Math Handbook pages 38–39

Differentiation in Investigation 4

Mathematics in This Investigation

The mathematics focuses on solving multistep problems using all four operations.

Understanding the Mathematics

Students break down multistep problems into all of the steps needed to complete the solution. They carefully keep track of their work and are aware of what parts of the problem they've answered and what work they still need to do. They use answers they've already found to help them solve new problems. Students know which operation to use in solving problems, and they efficiently and flexibly use strategies for all four operations.

Option: Assign the **Extension** activity.

Partially Understanding the Mathematics

Students break down multistep problems into different steps, but they might not solve all parts of the problems posed. They are less careful about keeping track of their work, and after solving several problems, they are uncertain about what questions they've answered or what they still need to solve. Students usually don't notice the relationships between problems, and rather than using what they've already answered, they often treat each problem as new. Students know which operation to use in solving problems. They are likely to be efficient and accurate for all the operations except division.

Option: Assign the **Practice** activity.

Not Understanding the Mathematics

Students are often overwhelmed by the amount of information given in the questions. They are uncertain where to start or how to find the answers. They might randomly pick numbers and operations and then believe they've answered the questions. Students generally know whether the problem is asking them to add or subtract, but they are less certain about multiplication and division. They are likely to be somewhat efficient in solving addition problems, but they are less efficient and accurate with the other operations.

Option: Assign the **Intervention** activity.

Investigation 4 Quiz

In addition to your observations and students' work in Investigation 4, the Quiz (R61) can be used to gather more information.

Name _____ Date _____

How Many People? How Many Teams?

Quiz

Use the chart to choose the correct answer.

Pet Food	Cans per Case	Price per Case
Cat food	36	$55
Dog food	32	$49

1. A pet store placed an order for 504 cans of cat food. How many cases is that?

   A. 9 cases   **B.** 10 cases   **C.** 14 cases   **D.** 16 cases

2. A pet hospital ordered 16 cases of dog food. What was the total cost of the dog food?

   A. $880   **B.** $816   **C.** $784   **D.** $512

3. Last year, a cat shelter purchased 5 cases of cat food per week. What was the total cost for the year? (Hint: There are 52 weeks in 1 year.)

   A. $275   **B.** $1,925   **C.** $12,740   **D.** $14,300

4. A kennel spent $3,300 for cat food and $2,205 for dog food. How many cases of pet food were purchased?

   A. 112 cases   **B.** 105 cases   **C.** 100 cases   **D.** 60 cases

5. A dog breeder uses 48 cans of dog food a day. How long will 35 cases of dog food last? Show your work, using clear and concise notation.
   A little more than 23 days; review students' work.

Use after Session 4.5.   Unit 7 **R61**

Intervention

20 MIN   PAIRS

Solving Multistep Problems

Use anytime after Session 4.1.

Math Focus Points

◆ Solving multistep word problems

◆ Solving 2-digit by 2-digit or 3-digit multiplication problems fluently

Materials: chart paper

. . . .

Materials to Prepare: Write each story in the activity on chart paper.

Draw students' attention to the first story.

> There are 88 students in the 5th grade at Kennedy School. The principal bought one glue stick and one ruler for each 5th grader. The glue sticks cost 45¢ each. The rulers cost 32¢ each. What was the total cost?

Can you do just one computation to find the total cost? Allow students to discuss this with a partner and share their thoughts. Reread the problem as needed and help students understand that they cannot simply pull numbers from the problem and find the answer with a single computation. What information do you need in order to find the total cost?

Students might say:

"You need to know the cost of all the glue sticks and the cost of all the rulers."

Let's start with the glue sticks. How can you figure out the cost of all the glue sticks? After students respond, give them time to solve that part of the problem. Be sure students know how to express the answer as dollars and cents. Tell students to record

the answer to this part of the problem clearly on their paper because they will need it to complete the problem.

In a similar manner, have students find the cost of the rulers. Again, have them clearly record the answer to this part of the problem. Now you're ready to figure out the total cost. What operation will you use? What numbers will you use? Where can you find those numbers? What's the answer to the problem?

Students might say:

"I need to add $39.60 and $28.16. That's the cost of the glue sticks and the cost of the rulers. $39.60 + $28.16 = $67.76. The total cost is $67.76."

Have pairs work together on the next story. Remind them to think about the smaller parts of the problem that they need to solve before they can answer the question in the problem.

> Kennedy School has 14 classrooms. Polk School has 18 classrooms. Each classroom at the schools is getting 28 new student desks. What is the total number of new student desks at the two schools?

ELL ▶ **English Language Learners**

Rephrase Story problems can be especially difficult for English Language Learners. As you read the stories, rephrase sentences to eliminate extra information. Also, address any unfamiliar words that may cause confusion.

Additional Resource

Student Math Handbook page 36

Practice

20 MIN   PAIRS

Multistep Problems

Use anytime after Session 4.2.

Math Focus Points

◆ Using all four operations to solve problems

Materials: chart paper, R62

Name _____ Date _____

How Many People? How Many Teams?

Multistep Problems

Solve the problems below. Show your work. Be sure to write your answer clearly. **Review students' work.**

1. A lawn service mows 18 lawns a day. They are paid $28 for each lawn they mow. How much does the lawn service earn in a 5-day week? **$2,520**

2. Georgia has a bag of 144 beads and two bags with 180 beads in each bag. She uses 28 beads to make a necklace. How many necklaces can she make with the beads she has? **18 necklaces**

3. Walter had new carpeting installed in his 13-foot by 18-foot family room. They paid $7 per square foot for the carpet and $2 per square foot for the pad under the carpet. What was the total cost for the carpet and pad? **$2,106**

4. A factory made 9,900 bars of soap. They wrapped 6 bars in a package. Then they put 48 packages in a box. How many boxes were completely filled? **34 boxes**

R62 Unit 7   Use anytime after Session 4.2.

. . . .

Materials to Prepare: Write each story in the activity on chart paper.

Draw students' attention to the first story.

> Olivia bought 4 trays of flowers and 16 flowerpots. Each tray contains 36 flowers. She wants the same number of flowers in each flowerpot. How many flowers should she plant in each pot?

Can you do just one computation to answer the question in the problem? What do you need to figure out before you can answer it?

Students might say:

"You have to figure out how many flowers she has in all."

How can you find how many flowers Olivia has? What should you do next to answer the question in the problem? Have students solve the problem and discuss the results.

Ask students to read the next story.

> Joshua hired a company to install a fence around his 42-foot by 50-foot backyard. The fencing cost $4 per foot. The labor charge was $350. What was Joshua's total cost for the fence?

Have pairs discuss how they would solve the problem. Ask volunteers to describe their plans. Then students solve the problem and discuss the results.

Distribute copies of Multistep Problems (R62).

ELL English Language Learners

Provide a Word List English Language Learners may have difficulty with these stories due to their unfamiliarity with some of the words. Write the words *flower, flowerpot, plant, company, install, fence,* and *labor* on chart paper. Explain the meaning and draw a picture for each. Post this list in the classroom for reference.

Additional Resource

Student Math Handbook page 36

Extension

30 MIN GROUPS

Finding the Best Buy
Use anytime after Session 4.1.

Math Focus Points

◆ Solving multistep word problems

◆ Solving 2-digit by 2-digit or 3-digit multiplication problems fluently

◆ Solving division problems with a 2-digit divisor fluently

Materials: chart paper, R63

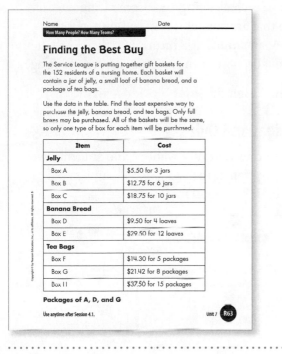

Materials to Prepare: Copy the table shown in the activity onto chart paper.

There are 286 students at Holmes School. The school held a fundraiser to purchase a T-shirt and a cap for each student to wear in the variety show. There are different choices, which are shown in the table. Only full packages may be purchased. In order for all of the students to be dressed alike, only one type of package for T-shirts and one for caps will be purchased.

Item	Cost
T-shirts	
Package A	$119 for package of 6
Package B	$149 for package of 8
Package C	$225 for package of 12
Caps	
Package D	$66 for package of 8
Package E	$162 for package of 20

Work in your groups to come up with the least expensive way to purchase the T-shirts and caps. *(Purchase 36 of Package B and 36 of Package D)* Have students share their findings. If any students come up with different results, work together to resolve the discrepancies.

Ask students to figure out the cost per cap for each package of caps. Package E offers the less expensive cost per cap, but purchasing 36 of package D is less expensive than purchasing 15 of Package E. Ask groups to conjecture why this is the case.

Students might say:

"If you choose package D, you wind up buying 2 caps you don't need. But if you choose package E, you're paying for 14 caps you don't need."

Distribute copies of Finding the Best Buy (R63).

ELL ▸ **English Language Learners**

Model Thinking Aloud Some students may have difficulty verbalizing their solution process. Work through each step with them as you model your thinking aloud. First, I found how much it would cost for each package. Then, I looked to see which T-shirt package and which cap package cost the least.

Additional Resource

Student Math Handbook page 37

Differentiation in Investigation 1

Mathematics in This Investigation

The mathematics focuses on using graphs and tables to represent and describe rates of change that are constant as well as rates of change that are not constant but can be determined.

Understanding the Mathematics

Students create a graph and a table that match a story about a child's height over some number of years given a few facts and the rate of growth. They are comfortable with words that describe rate of change (e.g., *quickly, slowly, steadily*) and can visualize how such words would be represented on a graph or in a table of height data. They compare rates of change by comparing the steepness of the lines on graphs representing growth. They accurately interpret situations about constant growth and about growth that is not constant but is predictable. Students can describe, in a general way, how an imaginary animal's growth is changing, and they use that rule to reason about what the animal's height will be at future ages and, possibly, at any age.

Option: Assign the **Extension** activity.

Partially Understanding the Mathematics

When given a story about a child's height over time, students may find it challenging to make a graph and a table that show the same story. They are developing an understanding of how words that describe rate of change (e.g., *quickly, slowly, steadily*) relate to the steepness of lines on a graph. They accurately interpret situations about constant growth and about growth that is not constant but is predictable, using particular numbers to describe the way an animal's growth is changing. To figure out the height of an animal at future ages, students start with known data. Then they either add each additional year's growth, or they multiply to find the growth over a number of years and add that to the current data.

Option: Assign the **Practice** activity.

Not Understanding the Mathematics

Students are just beginning to think about how words that describe rate of change (e.g., *quickly, slowly, steadily*) relate to how a graph looks, so they have a hard time creating a graph or table to match a given story about a child's height over time. Their tables and graphs are not likely to correctly show the values and change over time. Students are still developing fluency with plotting points on a graph. They are developing their ability to interpret and describe one graph or situation. Comparing rates of change is challenging, as is comparing rates of change that are not constant. To figure out the height of an animal at a future age, they likely figure out many or most of the heights at intervening ages.

Option: Assign the **Intervention** activity.

Investigation 1 Quiz

In addition to your observations and students' work in Investigation 1, the Quiz (R64) can be used to gather more information.

Name _____ **Date** _____ ✔
Growth Patterns

Quiz

Use the graph to choose the correct answer.

Growth of Creatures X and Z

1. How tall was Creature X at birth?
   A. 2 cm
   B. 3 cm
   C. 10 cm
   D. 22 cm

2. When Creature Z was 12 cm tall, how old was it?
   A. 5 years   B. 3 years   C. 1 year   D. 3 months

3. Which is **not** true about Creature X's and Creature Z's growth?
   A. Creature X's growth was steady.
   B. Creature Z grew a different amount each year.
   C. At birth, Creature X was taller than Creature Z.
   D. Creature Z's growth slowed down as he got older.

4. How much did Creature X grow in 5 years?
   A. 2 cm   B. 5 cm   C. 10 cm   D. 12 cm

5. Did Creature Z's height ever catch up to Creature X's height? How can you tell that from the graph?
   Yes; answers will vary. Review students' work.

R64 Unit 8   Use after Session 1.5.

Intervention

Growth Table and Graph

Use anytime after Session 1.3.

Math Focus Points

◆ Identifying points in a graph with corresponding values in a table and interpreting the numerical information in terms of the situation the graph represents

◆ Finding the value of one quantity in a situation with a constant rate of change, given the value of the other (e.g., if you know the age, what is the height?)

Vocabulary: graph, plot

Materials: R65

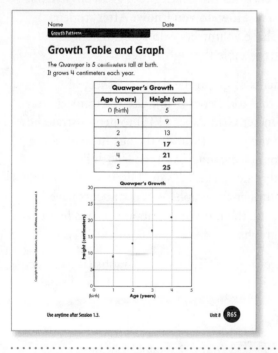

This activity focuses on the skills students need to complete *Student Activity Book* pages 9–11 and the rest of the growth problems in this unit.

Give each student a copy of Growth Table and Graph (R65). Draw students' attention to the table. *What information is given in the table? How can you figure out how tall the Quawper is when it is 3 years old? How can you find the other missing numbers?* Have students complete the table.

How many centimeters does the Quawper grow in 5 years? How do you know?

Students might say:

"It's 5 centimeters when it's born, and 25 centimeters when it's 5. $25 - 5 = 20$, so in 5 years it grows 20 centimeters."

"The Quawper grows 4 centimeters a year. $5 \times 4 = 20$, so that's 20 centimeters in 5 years."

Let's make a graph. How do you plot a point to represent 0 years and 5 centimeters? Help students first find 0 years and then move up to 5 centimeters.

When students are ready to plot the data in the next row of the table, discuss the process in more detail. You move *across* the graph to the number in the first column. Then you move *up* to the number in the second column. The heights are labeled 0, 5, 10, 15, and so on. How do you know where 9 cm should be? Have students complete the graph.

⬤ **ELL** ⬤ **English Language Learners**

Use Repetition As every point is plotted on the graph, repeat the process of how to plot a point and use movements to emphasize the directional words *across* and *up*. Encourage students to verbalize the movements as they plot their own points.

Additional Resource

Student Math Handbook pages 70–71

Practice

20 MIN   INDIVIDUALS

Tables and Graphs

Use anytime after Session 1.3.

Math Focus Points

◆ Identifying points in a graph with corresponding values in a table and interpreting the numerical information in terms of the situation the graph represents

◆ Describing the relationship between two quantities in a situation with a constant rate of change, taking into account a beginning amount and a constant increase (or decrease)

◆ Finding the value of one quantity in a situation with a constant rate of change, given the value of the other (e.g., if you know the age, what is the height?)

Materials: colored pencils, M8, T13, R66

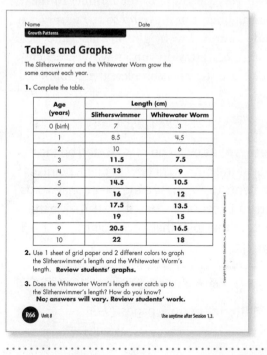

Gladeglider's Growth	
Age (years)	Length (cm)
0 (birth)	4
1	6.5
2	9
3	
4	

The Gladeglider grows the same amount every year. How can you figure out how long it is when it is 3 years old? How about when it is 4 years old? Record student responses in the table. How many centimeters does the Gladeglider grow in 5 years? In 10 years? How do you know? After students respond, have volunteers help you extend and complete the table through 10 years.

Ask students to graph the data on a sheet of Centimeter Grid Paper (M8). Use the transparency of Centimeter Grid Paper (T13) to demonstrate how to set up the graph. Indicate the age in years along the bottom of the graph and the length in centimeters along the left side. Discuss a reasonable way to number the graph. When students have finished, ask them questions about various features of their graphs.

Distribute copies of Tables and Graphs (R66). Each student will need another copy of M8 to complete R66.

Write the following table on the board. Continue it through 10 years, providing the lengths only through 2 years.

Additional Resource

Student Math Handbook pages 70–71

Extension

20 MIN | PAIRS

Making Rules
Use anytime after Session 1.3.

Math Focus Points

◆ Describing the relationship between two quantities in a situation with a constant rate of change, taking into account a beginning amount and a constant increase (or decrease)

Materials: *Student Activity Book* pp. 9–10, chart paper

....

Materials to Prepare: Copy the tables shown in the activity onto chart paper.

This activity gives students more opportunities for using rules to describe a situation with a constant rate of change.

Look at your answer to Problem 2 on *Student Activity Book* page 10. Can you find a rule that would work for *any* number of years? Use words or an expression. Record student responses on the board, getting both words and an expression.

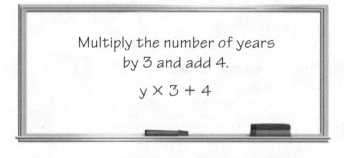

Multiply the number of years by 3 and add 4.

y × 3 + 4

Suppose the Flickerbill keeps growing at the same rate to an age of 150 years. Use one of the rules to find its height when it is 150 years old. Would you get the same answer using the other rule? How are these rules the same? How are they different? Why is there a 3 in both rules? Why is there a 4?

Students might say:

"The rule has to have a 3 because the Flickerbill grows 3 centimeters every year. The 4 is put in because it is 4 centimeters when it's born."

The rule must show the starting amount and the amount that changes each year. Do you think you could use the same kind of rule for animals who don't grow the same amount each year?

Students might say:

"No. In our rules, you multiply by the amount of growth each year. If that keeps changing, you don't know what to multiply by."

Show students the two tables below. Discuss the information shown in each table. Then, have pairs determine a general rule for each one. Challenge students to write the rule both in words and in an arithmetic expression.

Podpacer's Growth		Amusement Park Costs	
Age (years)	Length (cm)	Number of Rides	Total Cost
0 (birth)	4	0 (entrance fee)	$18
1	12	1	$20
2	20	2	$22
3	28	3	$24
4	36	4	$26

ELL **English Language Learners**

Provide a Word List Write the words *rule* and *rate* on the board. Discuss the meaning of each prior to beginning the activity. Some English Language Learners may confuse *rule* with the way they should behave. Explain that, in math, a *rule* describes how numbers behave. Also, be sure students understand that a *constant rate of change* means that the amount by which something changes stays the same.

Additional Resource

Student Math Handbook page 77

Differentiation in Investigation 2

Mathematics in This Investigation

The mathematics focuses on using graphs and tables to compare growth patterns and to represent these patterns using written and symbolic rules.

Additional Resource: *Representing Change,* pages 120–124 (See Curriculum Unit 8)

Understanding the Mathematics

Students use multiplication and their knowledge about the structure of an array to find the area and perimeter of different numbers of rows of square tiles. They understand and show or explain why the perimeter grows by 2 each time a row is added and why the area grows differently. Students use words and notation to write rules for determining the area or perimeter of a certain number of rows and for any number of rows. They are comfortable graphing data, have an accurate sense of what the graph will look like, and describe and compare graphs in useful ways. Students write rules for situations with a starting amount. They understand the difference between graphs with straight lines and those that curve.

Option: Assign the **Extension** activity.

Partially Understanding the Mathematics

Students may add or skip count to find the area and perimeter of different numbers of rows of square tiles, but they quickly begin to think in terms of multiplication. They see and use patterns, but they have to work to make sense of why the patterns exist and to connect those patterns to the actual tiles. Students use words, and maybe some notation, to describe how to determine the area or perimeter of a certain number of rows. A rule for any number of rows is challenging. They are comfortable graphing data but may not know what to expect before plotting the points. They describe and compare graphs in useful ways. They are developing their understanding of why their perimeter graphs increase by 2 and are parallel.

They notice that their area graphs are steep and that other graphs curve.

Option: Assign the **Practice** activity.

Not Understanding the Mathematics

Students mainly think in terms of addition as they find the area and perimeter of different numbers of rows of square tiles. They may know that the perimeter grows by 2 with each additional row but are unsure why that is true. Similarly, while their ability to plot such data is improving, they may not understand why the perimeter and area grow in different ways or why the graphs look different. Writing a general rule for a particular number of rows (or rounds) is very challenging, as is dealing with a situation that involves a starting amount or change that is not constant.

Option: Assign the **Intervention** activity.

Investigation 2 Quiz

In addition to your observations and students' work in Investigation 2, the Quiz (R67) can be used to gather more information.

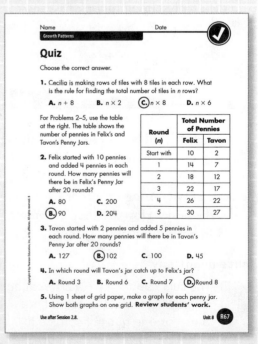

Intervention

30 MIN   INDIVIDUALS

Tile Rectangles

Use anytime after Session 2.1.

Math Focus Points

◆ Writing an arithmetic expression for finding the value of one quantity in terms of the other in a situation with a constant rate of change

◆ Making rules that relate one variable to the other in situations with a constant rate of change

◆ Using symbolic letter notation to represent the value of one variable in terms of another variable

Vocabulary: rule

Materials: color tiles (40 per student), R68

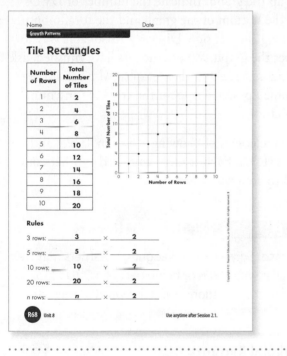

Some students need to concentrate on fewer aspects of the growth patterns generated by building tile rectangles. This activity focuses on just the total number of tiles.

Give each student a copy of Tile Rectangles (R68). Ask students to build a 1-row rectangle with 2 tiles in the row. Have them record the total number of tiles in the table. Continue with rows 2 through 10, all with 2 tiles per row. Ask students to describe the pattern they see in the second column of the table.

Draw students' attention to the rules under the table. When there are 3 rows, how can you find the total number of tiles? As students respond, have them record the numbers on the blanks. Similarly, discuss the expressions for 5 rows and 10 rows. How can you find the total number of tiles for 20 rows? Have students record it and then build a 20-row rectangle to check. Who can say in words what rule we could use to find the number of tiles for any row?

Students might say:

"Each row has 2 tiles. Multiply the number of rows by 2."

We can also write this as an arithmetic expression. If *n* stands for the number of rows, what do you have to multiply *n* by to get the total number of tiles? Have students complete the last rule and write it on the board. ($2 \times n$)

Have students graph the data in the table. Remind them that to plot each point, they move across the graph to the number in the first column. Then they move up to the number in the second column. When students are finished, ask what they notice about the graph.

ELL English Language Learners

Suggest a Sequence Some students may be confused when asked to plot a point on a graph. Review the words *plot*, *point*, and *graph* with students. On chart paper, write the following sequence of steps to help them.

1. Look at the number in the first column. Move that many spaces *across* the graph.

2. Look at the number in the second column. Move that many spaces *up* the graph.

3. Make a dot after moving across and up.

Additional Resource

Student Math Handbook page 77

Practice

🕐 **25 MIN** 👥 **PAIRS**

Showing Costs In Tables and Graphs

Use anytime after Session 2.7.

Math Focus Points

◆ Identifying points in a graph with corresponding values in a table and interpreting the numerical information in terms of the situation the graph represents

Materials: colored pencils, M8, T13, R69

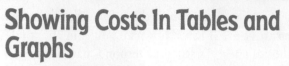

Name _____ Date _____
Growth Patterns

Showing Costs In Tables and Graphs

At Jolly Days Amusement Park, a child under 12 pays a $10 entrance fee and $3 for each ride. A person 12 years and older pays a $20 entrance fee and $2 for each ride.

1. Complete the table.

2. Use 1 grid and 2 different colors to graph the costs shown in the table. Show the number of rides along the bottom of your graph and the costs along the side. **Review students' work.**

3. Do the graphs cross each other? What does that mean? **Yes; For 10 rides, the total cost for a child under 12 is the same as for a person 12 or older.**

4. The amusement park also offers an all-day pass that is good for any number of rides. The pass costs $20. The customer still has to pay the entrance fee. If you were going to the park, would you buy the all-day pass? Explain your thinking. **Answers will vary. Review students' work.**

Number of Rides	Total Cost	
	Under 12 years old	12 years and older
0 (entrance fee)	$10	$20
1	$13	$22
2	$16	$24
3	$19	$26
4	$22	$28
5	$25	$30
10	$40	$40
15	$55	$50
20	$70	$60

Use anytime after Session 2.7.   Unit 8 **R69**

Write the following table on the board.

Deon's DVD Club	
Number of DVDs	Total Cost for 1 month
0 (monthly fee)	$3
1	$5
2	$7
3	
4	
5	

I belong to Deon's DVD Club. Each month, I pay $3. I also pay $2 for each DVD I rent. Have students help you complete the table. Be sure they understand that if 0 DVDs are rented, the monthly cost is $3. This is the "starting amount."

What would be the total monthly cost if I rent 10 DVDs? 15 DVDs? 20 DVDs? How did you figure it out? After students respond, extend the table and record the data for 10 DVDs, 15 DVDs, and 20 DVDs.

Ask students to graph the data on a sheet of Centimeter Grid Paper (M8). Use the transparency of Centimeter Grid Paper (T13) to demonstrate how to set up the graph. Indicate the number of DVDs along the bottom of the graph and the total monthly cost along the left side. Discuss a reasonable way to number the graph. When students have finished, ask them questions about their graphs. Also ask if they can come up with a rule for the costs for any number of DVDs.

Distribute copies of Showing Costs In Tables and Graphs (R69). Each student will need another copy of M8 to complete R69.

ELL English Language Learners

Rephrase Some English Language Learners may be unfamiliar with DVDs or being part of a DVD Club. Rephrase the questions using the word *movies*.

Additional Resource 📖

Student Math Handbook pages 72–73

Extension

20 MIN **PAIRS**

Area and Perimeter Rules

Use anytime after Session 2.4.

Math Focus Points

◆ Using symbolic letter notation to represent the value of one variable in terms of another variable

. . . .

This activity extends students' work with writing rules to include rules with two variables.

Let's think about some of the area rules for the rectangles you've built with tiles. What rule can you use to find the total number of tiles in *n* rows when there are 3 tiles per row? Can you express that as a simple expression with a variable?

Similarly, ask students to give rules for rectangles with 4, 5, 6, and 10 tiles per row. Summarize the rules on the board.

> Total number of tiles in *n* rows
>
> 3 tiles per row: $n \times 3$
>
> 4 tiles per row: $n \times 4$
>
> 5 tiles per row: $n \times 5$
>
> 6 tiles per row: $n \times 6$
>
> 10 tiles per row: $n \times 10$

Now I want you to think about a rule you can use to find the total number of tiles for any number of rows *and* any number of tiles per row. Talk this over with your partner. Pick another variable to represent the number of tiles per row. After students have had a chance to discuss this, ask them to share their rules.

Students might say:

"We picked the variable *t* for the number of tiles in a row. You have to multiply the number of rows by the number of tiles in a row, so our rule is $n \times t$."

Write this rule under the other rules on the board. Discuss how students can check if the expression is reasonable by testing some specific values.

Now think about the perimeter rules you've written. Work with your partner. Write a rule with a variable that you can use for finding the number of tiles in the perimeter of a rectangle with *n* rows when there are 3 tiles per row. Then write rules for rectangles with 4, 5, 6, and 10 tiles per row.

Use the same variable you used before to represent the number of tiles per row. Write a rule for finding the number of tiles in the perimeter of a rectangle with any number of rows *and* any number of tiles per row. *(2 × (n + t) −4, or an equivalent expression)*

ELL **English Language Learners**

Use Repetition Be sure students can relate the word form of a rule to a rule that uses symbols. For example, say, *The rule n × 3 means the number of rows times 3.* Have students practice translating symbolic rules into words and vice versa.

Additional Resource

Student Math Handbook page 78

Differentiation in Investigation 1

Mathematics in This Investigation

The mathematics focuses on collecting, representing, interpreting, and analyzing data.

Additional Resource: *Data Terms and Representations,* pages 113–114 (See Curriculum Unit 9)

Understanding the Mathematics

Students describe the shape of a set of data using aspects such as where the data are concentrated, the highest and lowest values, the range, and outliers. They accurately determine the median and connect it to the situation (e.g., half of the people balanced for less than this many seconds, and half balanced for longer). They use a variety of these aspects to compare two sets of data and draw conclusions that are based on evidence that they can point out in the data.

Option: Assign the **Extension** activity.

Partially Understanding the Mathematics

Students describe the shape of a set of data using aspects such as where the data are concentrated, the highest and lowest values, the range, and outliers. They accurately determine the median, though they may still be developing an understanding of how it connects to the situation. When they compare two sets of data, they may compare only a few aspects of the data. They can point to evidence that supports their conclusions, but they may still be working to develop their ability to compare two sets of data in a variety of ways in order to summarize what the data show.

Option: Assign the **Practice** activity.

Not Understanding the Mathematics

Students are still developing their ability to describe the shape of one set of data using a variety of aspects such as where the data are concentrated, the highest and lowest values, the range, and outliers. Accurately determining the median may be a challenge, and they likely don't yet understand what that measure tells them about a set of data. When comparing two sets of data, they can draw conclusions and point to the evidence in the data but they mainly rely on only one aspect of the data (e.g., the highest value) in their comparison.

Option: Assign the **Intervention** activity.

Investigation 1 Quiz

In addition to your observations and students' work in Investigation 1, the Quiz (R70) can be used to gather more information.

Name _____ Date _____

How Long Can You Stand on One Foot? ✓

Quiz

Choose the correct answer.

For Problems 1–5, use the line plots below. They show the number of students in each classroom at 2 schools.

King School: Classroom Sizes (number of students)

Edison School: Classroom Sizes (number of students)

1. How many classrooms at King School have 24 students?
   A. 0   **B.** 1   C. 2   D. 3

2. How many classrooms at Edison School have more than 30 students?
   A. 4   B. 3   **C.** 2   D. 1

3. What is the range of the class sizes at King School?
   A. 14   **B.** 15   C. 16   D. 24

4. What is the median of the class sizes at Edison School?
   A. 25   B. 24   C. 14   D. 9

5. Which school has larger classes? Explain your thinking.
   Edison School; review students' work.

R70 Unit 9   Use after Session 1.4.

Intervention

30 MIN   PAIRS

Comparing Data

Use anytime after Session 1.3.

Math Focus Points

◆ Comparing sets of data using the shape and spread of the data

◆ Developing arguments based on data

Vocabulary: data, line plot, median, range

Materials: R71

Name _____ Date _____

How Long Can You Stand on One Foot?

Comparing Data

Class Balancing Data

0 10 20 30 40 50 60 70 80 90 100 110 120 130 140 150
Students: Time Balanced on Left Foot (seconds)

0 10 20 30 40 50 60 70 80 90 100 110 120 130 140 150
Adults: Time Balanced on Left Foot (seconds)

Ways to describe the data	Students	Adults
How many in the group	21	20
Median	18	16
Range	120	145
Lowest number	5	2
Highest number	125	147
Concentration	clump around 14	clump around 9

Use anytime after Session 1.3.   Unit 9 **R71**

Write the following data on the board.

> Student Data: 5, 8, 10, 10, 14, 14, 14, 16, 18, 18, 18, 22, 22, 27, 27, 32, 40, 47, 70, 105, 125
>
> Adult Data: 2, 2, 4, 4, 4, 9, 12, 12, 12, 16, 16, 27, 27, 30, 33, 35, 51, 58, 71, 147

Give each student a copy of Comparing Data (R71). Tell students that the balancing data shown is for another fifth-grade class.

Tell students that the data shown on the board are represented in the line plots. Look at the data for students in the first line plot. Let's make a list of some of the ways we can describe these data. Record students' suggestions on the board as students copy them onto R71.

How many in the group	Lowest number
Median	Highest number
Range	Concentration

Using just the first line plot, have pairs work together to find a numerical value for each descriptor you listed on the board. Ask them to record their results on their papers and share their findings. Remind them to use the numbers on the board to help them identify the value of each point on the line plots, if needed.

Then have students work with the second line plot. Have them provide numerical values for the same descriptors and record their results. Discuss students' findings.

Now that we have values for the same aspects of both line plots, we can use them to compare the two sets of data. Taking one descriptor at a time, have students make a comparison statement about the data sets. Then ask them to draw a conclusion, if possible, about which group is made up of better balancers.

ELL English Language Learners

Provide a Word List Write the words *data, line plot, median,* and *range* on chart paper. Using a small data set, review the meaning of each.

Additional Resource

Student Math Handbook page 86

Practice

25 MIN   PAIRS

Comparing Fitness Tests

Use anytime after Session 1.3.

Math Focus Points

◆ Comparing sets of data using the shape and spread of the data

◆ Developing arguments based on data

Vocabulary: data, line plot, range, median

Materials: chart paper or blank transparency, R72

Name _____ Date _____

How Long Can You Stand on One Foot?

Comparing Fitness Tests

These line plots show the results of the sit-and-reach fitness test in 2 fifth-grade gym classes.

Class A: Sit-and-reach (centimeters)

Class B: Sit-and-reach (centimeters)

1. For each class, find the range, median, low score, and high score.

Class A		Class B	
Range:	14	Range:	16
Median:	24	Median:	28
Low score:	21	Low score:	18
High Score:	35	High Score:	34

2. Which class had better scores? Explain why you think so.
Class B; answers will vary. Review students' work.

R72 Unit 9   Use anytime after Session 1.3.

Materials to Prepare: Copy the line plots in the activity onto chart paper or a blank transparency.

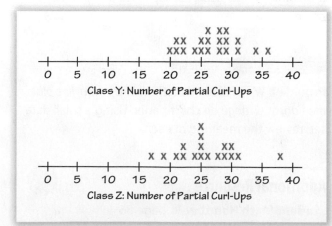

Class Y: Number of Partial Curl-Ups

Class Z: Number of Partial Curl-Ups

These line plots show the results of a partial-curl-up fitness test in two fifth-grade gym classes. Write three statements about how the two classes compare. Then work with a partner and share each statement. Make sure that each statement makes sense.

When pairs have finished the task, discuss the comparison statements they generated. Have students share any disagreements that came up when comparing statements. Make sure students have a clear understanding of why the statements were incorrect and how they can be corrected. Which class do you think had better scores? Why?

Students might say:

"Class Y did better. The median in this class is 26, and in Class Z, it is 25."

"The data are concentrated between 25 and 30 for Class Y and between 24 and 26 for Class Z. Class Y had better scores."

Distribute copies of Comparing Fitness Tests (R72).

(**ELL**) **English Language Learners**

Rephrase Remind students that the word *median* refers to the *middle of the data* when the data is put in *order*. The data used in the line plots for this activity and on R72 concern partial curl-ups and sit-and-reach. You might want to ask a student to demonstrate each one so that all students understand the names of these fitness events and can better understand the data.

Additional Resource

Student Math Handbook page 86

Extension

30 MIN PAIRS

More About Medians

Use anytime after Session 1.2.

Math Focus Points

◆ Using medians to compare groups

Some students can easily find the median of a data set, and they understand that the median splits the data into two equal-sized parts. These students can be challenged to break a data set into four equal-sized parts.

Write the following data set on the board.

2, 5, 5, 7, 10, 12, 12, 14, 15, 15, 20, 21

The Science Club held a car wash as a fundraiser. These data are the number of cars each student washed. Notice I've written the data in order. What is the median? What does the median mean in this situation?

Students might say:

"The median is 12. It means that half the kids washed 12 or fewer cars, and half washed 12 or more cars."

That's right. The median divides the data into two equal parts. Indicate the median in the data set written on the board.

2, 5, 5, 7, 10, 12, 12, 14, 15, 15, 20, 21

↑

12

Sometimes, mathematicians divide the data into four equal parts. To do this, they divide each half of the data in half again. Look at the bottom six numbers. What's the median of those numbers? Look at the top six numbers. What's the median of those numbers? As students respond, indicate those values in the data set.

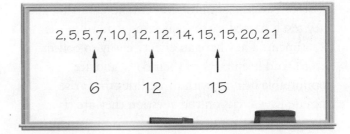

2, 5, 5, 7, 10, 12, 12, 14, 15, 15, 20, 21

↑   ↑   ↑

6   12   15

Now we have the data divided into fourths. 6 is called the *lower quartile*. 15 is the *upper quartile*. What do these quartiles mean with regard to the car washes?

Students might say:

"A fourth of the kids washed 6 or fewer cars. A fourth of the kids washed 15 or more cars."

Have pairs make up a story to match each data set below. Ask them find the median, lower quartile, and upper quartile of each set and use these values to describe the data in the context of their story.

Data Set 1: 24, 25, 27, 28, 29, 34, 36, 38

Data Set 2: 67, 74, 76, 76, 80, 84, 85, 87, 91, 96

ELL English Language Learners

Suggest a Sequence Review the meaning of the word *median*. Suggest a sequence of steps for finding the median. For example: *First,* write the data in order from least to greatest. *Then,* find the middle. This is the median.

Additional Resource

Student Math Handbook page 86

Differentiation in Investigation 2

Mathematics in This Investigation

The mathematics focuses on designing and carrying out a data investigation, and on representing and analyzing the resulting data.

Understanding the Mathematics

Students carefully design an experiment that will result in two sets of numerical data to compare, and they test a procedure for collecting data from the experiment. They have an effective way to collect, record, and keep track of their data, and are comfortable dealing with difficulties that arise because they focus on the question they are trying to answer. They can use different ways to represent data, and they choose a representation that makes comparing the two groups easy. They clearly communicate their findings and tie them to evidence in the data.

Option: Assign the **Extension** activity.

Partially Understanding the Mathematics

Students carefully design an experiment that will result in two sets of numerical data to compare. They have effective ways of recording and keeping track of data but may not be entirely consistent in the way that they are collecting the data. They are comfortable with at least one way to represent two data sets for comparison. Students' representations highlight the two groups and communicate the students' findings. Students may still be comparing only a few aspects of each set of data but they can point those out in their representation.

Option: Assign the **Practice** activity.

Not Understanding the Mathematics

Students work hard to design an experiment that will result in two sets of numerical data to compare. In their first attempts, they may choose categorical data, use questions with too many variables, or have trouble defining the comparison groups or measurements. Collecting, recording, and keeping track of the data is likely challenging. Students have trouble using a consistent procedure or seeing the need for it. They are comfortable with representing one set of data but they may still be developing an understanding of how to show two data sets in one representation. Students' findings likely focus on only one or two aspects of the data, and those aspects may not be the best for communicating the similarities and differences between the two sets of data.

Option: Assign the **Intervention** activity.

Investigation 2 Quiz

In addition to your observations and students' work in Investigation 2, the Quiz (R73) can be used to gather more information.

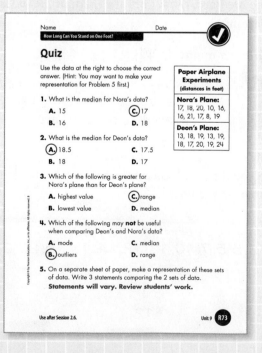

Intervention

25 MIN   INDIVIDUALS

Line Plots for Two Sets of Data

Use anytime after Session 2.3.

Math Focus Points

◆ Representing two sets of data in order to compare them

Vocabulary: line plot, scale, interval

Materials: T89 or *Student Activity Book* p. 13, rulers, R74

Name _____ Date _____
How Long Can You Stand on One Foot?

Line Plots for Two Sets of Data

Blue Car			Orange Car	
Trial	Distance (inches)		Trial	Distance (inches)
1	27		1	37
2	38		2	31
3	34		3	30
4	30		4	39
5	28		5	38
6	29		6	21
7	18		7	37
8	20		8	29
9	34		9	36
10	33		10	38

0 5 10 15 20 25 30 35 40
Distance Traveled by Blue Car (inches)

0 5 10 15 20 25 30 35 40
Distance Traveled by Orange Car (inches)

R74 Unit 9   Use anytime after Session 2.3.

Give students a copy of Line Plots for Two Sets of Data (R74). Tell students that the data come from an experiment where the student released toy cars down a ramp and measured how far each car traveled past the bottom of the ramp.

You are going to make two line plots to represent the data in the tables. Notice how one line plot is above the other. This makes it easier to compare the data when the line plots are completed.

Show students the transparency of Balancing Data from Another Fifth-Grade Class (T89), or have them refer to *Student Activity Book* page 13. Students can use the pair of completed line plots as a model. How are these two line plots similar?

Students might say:

"The numbers along the bottom are the same and they all line up. The titles are about the same, too."

Let's start with titles for your line plots. What information should it show? Be sure the titles show that the distance is measured in inches. They may write each title either above or below the number line. Remind students that they need to allow room for the Xs.

What's the greatest number in the data? What number would you show as the greatest number on the scales? Do you think you should number the scale by 5s or 10s? Work with students to understand that eight intervals of 5 would allow for more precise graphing than four intervals of 10. The spaces between the numbers need to be the same. What would work? Help students use their ruler to see that a half-inch is reasonable. Have students complete the scale for each line plot and then plot the data given in the tables.

ELL) **English Language Learners**

Provide a Word List Write the words *scale* and *interval* on chart paper. Explain that the *scale* is shown along the side and bottom of the line plot and the *interval* is what you count by to get from one number to the next. Some English Language Learners may confuse the meaning of scale with that of a scale used to measure weight.

Additional Resource

Student Math Handbook page 86

Practice

Comparing Data
Use anytime after Session 2.3.

Math Focus Points

◆ Representing two sets of data in order to compare them

Materials: yardstick, R75

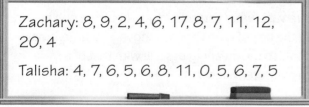

Name _____ Date _____

How Long Can You Stand on One Foot?

Comparing Data

The students in 2 classes were tested on right-angle push-ups. The results are shown in the line plots.

Room 204: Right-Angle Push-Ups

0   5   10   15   20   25   30

Room 109: Right-Angle Push-Ups

0   5   10   15   20   25   30

Complete the chart. For Problem 3, make your own choice about what to compare.

What are you comparing?	Room 204	Room 109	Who is better?
1. Median	18	13	Room 204
2. Highest value	23	19	Room 204
3.			

Answers will vary. Review students' work.

4. Who is better at right-angle push-ups? Why?

Room 204; answers will vary. Review students' work.

5. Why might the results be different for the 2 classes?

Answers will vary. Review students' work.

Use anytime after Session 2.3.   Unit 9   **R75**

· ·

Write the following data on the board.

> Zachary: 8, 9, 2, 4, 6, 17, 8, 7, 11, 12, 20, 4
>
> Talisha: 4, 7, 6, 5, 6, 8, 11, 0, 5, 6, 7, 5

For two weeks, Zachary and Talisha kept track of how many pieces of mail their family received each day. Let's make a line plot for each set of data.

On the board, set up two lines for the line plots, one above the other. Discuss a reasonable scale and title for the line plots. Why is it a good idea to use the same scale and to line up the numbers on the two line plots?

Have volunteers come to the board to write the titles and numbers for the scale. Encourage careful work using a yardstick to measure the lengths of the intervals.

Call on other students to graph the data on the line plots. If you take a quick look at the line plots, can you say what a typical amount of mail would be for each family? How can you tell?

Students might say:

"Zachary's family seems to get different amounts, but Talisha's family gets about 6 pieces a day. The Xs clump together around the 6."

It's a good idea to look for concentrations of the data. What are some other ways we could compare the two sets of data? As students offer suggestions, write them on the board.

> Median   Lowest number
>
> Range   Highest number

Find the value of each of those features for each set of data. Which family typically seems to get more mail in a day? How can you support that answer?

Distribute copies of Comparing Data (R75).

ELL English Language Learners

Rephrase Some English Language Learners may be unfamiliar with the word *concentration*. Explain that it means that there are a lot of something. Be aware that some students may confuse the meaning with other meanings, such as paying close attention to something.

Additional Resource

Student Math Handbook page 86

Extension

🕐 **30 MIN**   👫 **PAIRS**

Comparing Representations
Use anytime after Session 2.4.

Math Focus Points

◆ Representing two sets of data in order to compare them

◆ Considering how well a data representation communicates to an audience

Some students should be challenged to represent two data sets in more than one way. Let me tell you about a rubber band experiment a student in another class performed. He had a bag of blue rubber bands and a bag of red rubber bands. In each bag, the rubber bands appeared to be the same size. He wanted to know which were the stretchier rubber bands.

He tied a rubber band on the handle of a small bucket, put a 2-pound weight in the bucket, and hung the rubber band on a hook. He measured how long the rubber band stretched. He repeated the trial 15 times with blue rubber bands and 15 times with red rubber bands. Here are the data that give the lengths in centimeters for each type of rubber band.

Write the following data on the board.

> Blue rubber band: 13, 17, 16, 16, 12, 19, 17, 16, 13, 17, 14, 17, 15, 13, 17
>
> Red rubber band: 9, 12, 11, 9, 13, 11, 12, 12, 13, 12, 9, 10, 10, 15, 12

Work in pairs. Each of you should make a representation of the data. Talk about it first. Try to use a representation you haven't used yet in this unit. Also, don't make the same type of representation as your partner.

When you're done, you and your partner should evaluate the two representations. Ask yourselves two things. How easily can someone gather information from the representation? How easily can someone compare the two sets of data by using your representation? Then see if you both feel that one of your representations is better than the other.

After students complete these tasks, ask them to share their ideas and the representations they made. Which do you think is the better representation? Why?

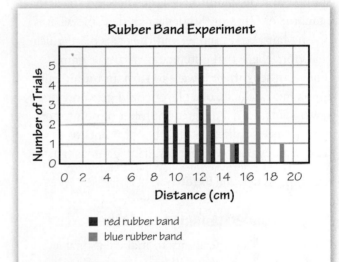

ELL English Language Learners

Provide Sentence Stems To help students verbalize their representations, provide sentence stems. For example: I represented the data by _____ . The representation I think is best is _____ because _____ .

Additional Resource 📖

Student Math Handbook pages 86–88

Differentiation in Investigation 3

Mathematics in This Investigation

The mathematics focuses on the probability associated with various spinner experiments and games (e.g., $\frac{1}{2}$ green, $\frac{1}{4}$ green, $\frac{3}{4}$ green) and what makes a game fair or unfair.

Understanding the Mathematics

Students make reasonable predictions about what will happen when a spinner is spun 50 times, and explain those predictions. They figure out the theoretical probability associated with a given spinner and distinguish between that and the actual outcome of 50 spins. Students can describe what is or isn't fair about a game, and they can distinguish that from the actual outcome of a sample game. They can see different ways to turn an unfair game into a fair one (e.g., one player could get more or fewer spins, earn a different number of points per turn, or need a different number of points to win). They can explain why the resulting game is fair.

Option: Assign the **Extension** activity.

Partially Understanding the Mathematics

Students develop the ability to make reasonable predictions about what will happen when a spinner is spun 50 times. They can figure out the theoretical probability associated with a given spinner, but they may occasionally have trouble reconciling this with a trial that does not give that result. They can describe what is or isn't fair about a game, particularly after playing. Again, though, the results of a sample game can occasionally override what students know about the theoretical fairness of the game. Students find and can explain one way to turn an unfair game into a fair one, but they may have trouble seeing that there are other ways to do so.

Option: Assign the **Practice** activity.

Not Understanding the Mathematics

Students' estimates of what will happen when a spinner is spun 50 times may seem like random guesses, particularly at first. They have trouble figuring out theoretical probabilities because of the impact of the actual trials. Similarly, their ideas about fair and unfair games may rely more on the results of a particular experiment than the theoretical fairness of the game. Adapting an unfair game to be fair is challenging and likely involves a great deal of trial and error.

Option: Assign the **Intervention** activity.

Investigation 3 Quiz

In addition to your observations and students' work in Investigation 3, the Quiz (R76) can be used to gather more information.

Name _____ Date _____

How Long Can You Stand on One Foot? ✔

Quiz

Choose the correct answer.

For Problems 1–2, use the spinner at the right.

1. What is the probability of landing on gray?
   A. $\frac{1}{4}$ B. $\frac{1}{2}$ C. $\frac{2}{3}$ **D.** $\frac{3}{4}$

2. In 60 spins, about how many times is the spinner likely to land on gray?
   A. 45   B. 30   C. 15   D. 10

For Problems 3–4, use the spinner at the right.

3. What is the probability of landing on an even number?
   A. $\frac{1}{2}$ **B.** $\frac{2}{3}$ C. $\frac{3}{4}$ D. $\frac{5}{6}$

4. Player 1 and Player 2 use the spinner to play a game. Player 1 scores 4 points when the spinner lands on an odd number. In order to keep the game fair, how many points should Player 2 score when the spinner lands on an even number?
   A. 8 points   B. 4 points   **C.** 2 points   D. 1 point

5. Player 1 and Player 2 want to use the spinner at the right to play a game. Write a complete set of rules for a fair game.
   Answers will vary. Review students' work.

R76 Unit 9   Use after Session 3.5.

30 MIN   PAIRS

Intervention

Probability Experiment
Use anytime after Session 3.2.

Math Focus Points

◆ Comparing the expected probability of an event with the actual results of repeated trials of that event

◆ Carrying out multiple trials of an experiment

Vocabulary: probability, trial

Materials: connecting cubes (2 red and 1 blue per pair), bag

Show students 2 red cubes and 1 blue cube. Put the cubes in a bag. If I shake the bag, reach in without looking, and pick out a cube, which color am I more likely to get? What is the probability that I will pick a red cube? What is the probability that I will pick a blue cube? How did you figure out those probabilities? Write the probabilities on the board as students respond.

Students might say:

"2 out of 3 cubes are red, so that's a probability of $\frac{2}{3}$. 1 out of 3 cubes is blue, so that's a probability of $\frac{1}{3}$."

$$\frac{2}{3} \leftarrow \text{number of red cubes} \atop \leftarrow \text{total number of cubes}$$

$$\frac{1}{3} \leftarrow \text{number of blue cubes} \atop \leftarrow \text{total number of cubes}$$

Suppose after I pick a cube, I put it back in the bag, shake the bag, and pick a cube again. Demonstrate doing this several times. If I keep doing this over and over again, do you think I would get red more often, blue more often, or about the same? Why do you think so?

You and your partner are going to do an experiment where you pick a cube out of the bag 30 times. How many times do you predict you'll pull out a red cube? Why?

Give each pair a bag with 2 red cubes and 1 blue cube. Show students how to use tally marks to record the color in a table like the one below.

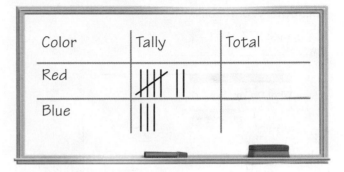

Have one student pick the cube for 30 trials as the other records the color. Ask students to compare their results to their predictions. If you conduct the experiment again, do you think you'll get the same results? Do you want to change your original prediction? Have partners reverse roles and conduct the same 30-trial experiment, again.

If you conduct the experiment a third time, what do you think will happen? When you know the probability of something, does that tell you *exactly* what you can expect to happen?

⬤ ELL ⬤ English Language Learners

Provide a Word List Write the words *probability*, *experiment, trial,* and *prediction* on chart paper. Read the list with students, have them repeat the words, and then explain each word. Have students practice using the words in sentences.

Additional Resource
Student Math Handbook pages 89–91

Practice

What Do You Expect?

Use anytime after Session 3.3.

Math Focus Points

◆ Comparing the expected probability of an event with the actual results of repeated trials of that event

Vocabulary: probability

Materials: R77

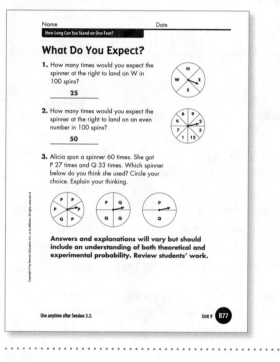

On the board, draw this spinner.

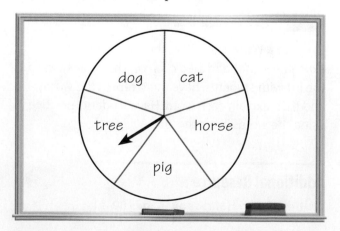

If all the sections are the same size, what is the probability that the spinner will land on a plant?

What is the probability that the spinner will land on an animal? How do you know?

Students might say:

 "There's only 1 section that has a plant. So the probability that it will land on a plant is $\frac{1}{5}$. There are 4 sections with animals. The probability that it will land on an animal is $\frac{4}{5}$."

Suppose I spin this spinner 100 times. How many times do you think it would land on a plant? How many times would you expect it to land on an animal? Why do you think so?

Students might say:

 "It should land on a plant about $\frac{1}{5}$ of the time since that's the probability. $\frac{1}{5}$ of 100 is 20. So that's 20 times. The rest of the time it would land on an animal. That's 80 times."

What if I told you that in 100 spins the spinner actually landed on a plant 17 times, and it landed on an animal 83 times? Do you think these results seem reasonable? When you know the probability of something, does that tell you *exactly* what you can expect to happen?

Distribute copies of What Do You Expect? (R77).

ELL **English Language Learners**

Suggest a Sequence Provide a format for sequencing the steps to find a probability. For example:

1. Count all the sections on the spinner.

2. Count how many sections show a [plant].

3. Use those numbers to write a fraction with the number of sections as the bottom number.

Additional Resource

Student Math Handbook pages 89–91

Extension

30 MIN   PAIRS

Designing Spinners

Use anytime after Session 3.4.

Math Focus Points

◆ Determining the fairness of a game based on the probability of winning for each player

Vocabulary: fair

Materials: scissors, paper clips, pencils, R78

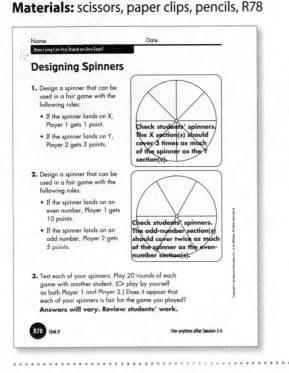

In this activity, students extend their work designing fair games. Rather than adjusting the rules of the game to fit a given spinner, they design a spinner to fit the rules of the game.

Draw a blank 6-section spinner on the board.

Suppose two students are playing a spinner game. If the spinner lands on a 1-digit number, Player 1 gets 8 points. If the spinner lands on a 2-digit number, Player 2 gets 4 points. How can you label this spinner so the game is fair? Talk about it with your partner.

After students have arrived at a solution, call on volunteers to draw their spinner and explain their thinking.

Students might say:

"1-digit numbers are worth twice as many points as 2-digit numbers. So to balance things out, we put 2-digit numbers in twice as many sections."

"We put 2-digit numbers in 2 sections, a 1-digit number in one section, and we filled the rest of the sections with 3-digit numbers."

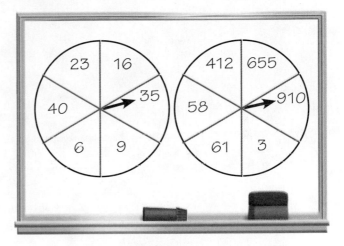

Distribute copies of Designing Spinners (R78). Students will need scissors, paper clips, and pencils to test their spinners.

ELL English Language Learners

Partner Talk Have ELL pairs explain how the spinner they created is *fair* or *unfair* to give them practice with English. Encourage more proficient speakers to use words like *points, 1-digit,* and *2-digit* in their explanations.

Additional Resource

Student Math Handbook page 92

Resource Masters

Quiz

Choose the correct answer.

1. Which multiplication combination is modeled by the array?

A. $4 \times 8 = 32$

B. $4 \times 7 = 28$

C. $4 \times 6 = 24$

D. $3 \times 7 = 21$

2. Which number is a prime number?

A. 51   **B.** 49   **C.** 31   **D.** 1

3. Which shows all the factors of 42?

A. 1, 2, 3, 6, 7, 14, 21, 42

B. 1, 2, 3, 4, 6, 7, 42

C. 2, 3, 6, 7, 14, 21

D. 1, 6, 7, 42

4. Which number fits all four clues?
Clue 1: This number is a multiple of 3.
Clue 2: This number is even.
Clue 3: This number is a square number.
Clue 4: This number is less than 50.

A. 9   **B.** 16   **C.** 30   **D.** 36

5. How can you use multiplication combinations for 24 to help you find multiplication combinations for 240?

Number Puzzles with 4 Clues

Solve each puzzle. If there is more than one number that works, list at least 2 numbers.

1. Clue 1: This number is a multiple of 4.
Clue 2: This number is greater than 20.
Clue 3: This number is less than 50.
Clue 4: The sum of the digits in this number is 9.

Number(s): _____

2. Clue 1: This number is a prime number.
Clue 2: This number is a factor of 63.
Clue 3: This number is less than 20.
Clue 4: This number is a factor of 14.

Number(s): _____

3. Clue 1: This number is a composite number.
Clue 2: This number is a factor of 48.
Clue 3: This number is an even number.
Clue 4: This number is less than 15.

Number(s): _____

4. Clue 1: This number is a square number.
Clue 2: This number is a multiple of 16.
Clue 3: This number is greater than 20.
Clue 4: This number is less than 80.

Number(s): _____

Number Puzzles and Multiple Towers

Prime Factorization

Write the prime factorization of each number.

1. 48 _____

480 _____

4,800 _____

9,600 _____

2. 560 _____

5,600 _____

11,200 _____

22,400 _____

3. Write 3 different ways you can multiply
2 factors to get a product of 22,400.

_____   _____   _____

Write 3 different ways you can multiply
3 factors to get a product of 22,400.

_____   _____   _____

4. How does the prime factorization of 22,400 help
you find the combinations you wrote in Problem 3?

Quiz

Choose the correct answer.

1. $9 \times 300 =$

    A. 27,000   **B.** 2,700   **C.** 2,100   **D.** 270

2. Which product is greater than 400×80?

    A. 700×8 **C.** 300×90

    B. 70×500 **D.** 40×800

3. $49 \times 24 =$

    A. 836   **B.** 1,076   **C.** 1,151   **D.** 1,176

4. Part of a student's solution for 28×67 is shown below.

    $20 \times 60 = 1,200$

    $20 \times 7 = 140$

    $8 \times 60 = 480$

Which step should the student do next?

    A. 8×7 **B.** 20×6 **C.** 80×7 **D.** 2×6

5. Draw an array to show how to find 32×25.

Name _____   Date _____

Multiplying 2-Digit by 2-Digit Numbers

Solve the problems below. Show your solutions clearly.

1. 23
$\times\ 9$

2. 17
$\times 64$

3. 44×30

4. 25×81

5. 90×70

6. 32×55

Number Puzzles and Multiple Towers

Multiplication Compare with Digit Cards

Write >, <, or = in each box. In the space to the right of each problem, write how you decided which product is greater.
Challenge: Try to compare products without finding the exact answer to the multiplication problems.

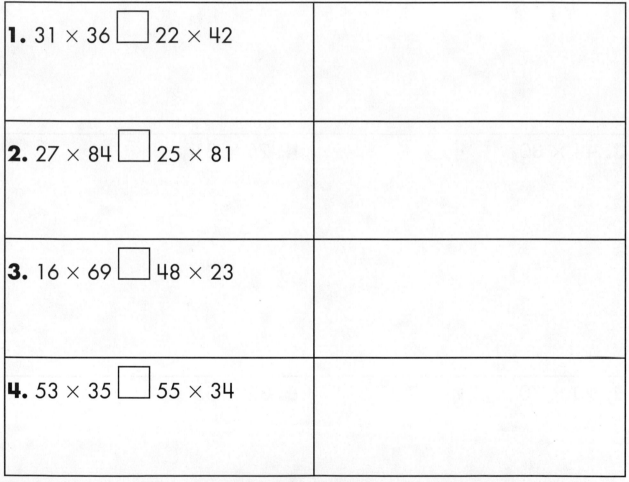

1. 31 × 36 ☐ 22 × 42	
2. 27 × 84 ☐ 25 × 81	
3. 16 × 69 ☐ 48 × 23	
4. 53 × 35 ☐ 55 × 34	

5. Use the digits 4, 1, 8, and 6 to make a 2-digit by 2-digit multiplication problem with the greatest product possible. How do you know this is the greatest product possible?

Use anytime after Session 2.4.

Quiz

Choose the correct answer.

1. 180 ÷ 18 =

    A. 5   **B.** 10   **C.** 20   **D.** 100

2. Which of the following is true?

    A. 200 ÷ 40 = 300 ÷ 50   **C.** 700 ÷ 90 < 400 ÷ 80

    B. 600 ÷ 80 < 720 ÷ 90   **D.** 500 ÷ 70 < 300 ÷ 60

3. 822 ÷ 35

    A. 32 R7   **B.** 23 R27   **C.** 23 R17   **D.** 22 R52

4. Part of a student's solution for 182 ÷ 14 is shown below.

      140 ÷ 14 = 10

      182 − 140 = 42

      42 ÷ 14 = 3

Which step should the student do next?

    A. 10 + 3   **C.** 10 + 42 + 3

    B. 140 ÷ 2   **D.** 10 − 3

5. Describe how to use a multiple tower to find 330 ÷ 22.

Building Multiple Towers

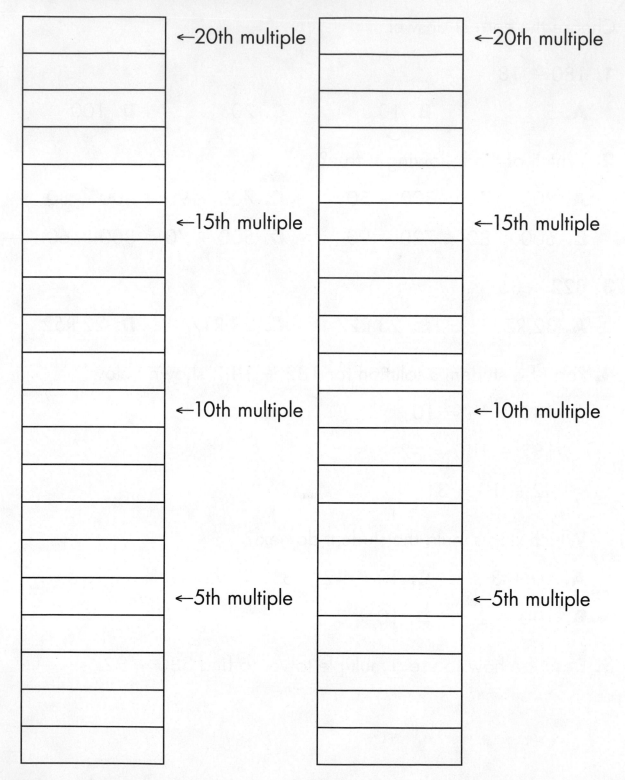

←20th multiple

←15th multiple

←10th multiple

←5th multiple

←20th multiple

←15th multiple

←10th multiple

←5th multiple

Dividing by 2-Digit Numbers

Solve the problems below. Show your solutions clearly.

1. 238 ÷ 14 _____

2. 713 ÷ 31 _____

3. 725 ÷ 18 _____

4. 250 ÷ 25 _____

5. 884 ÷ 26 _____

6. 210 ÷ 40 _____

7. Polk School has 420 student desks and 15 classrooms. Each classroom has the same number of desks. How many student desks are in each classroom?

_____

Quiz

Choose the correct answer.

1. How many cubes will fill the box shown
at the right?

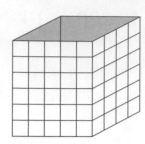

A. 20

C. 120

B. 100

D. 144

2. How many cubes will fill a box made with the
pattern shown at the right?

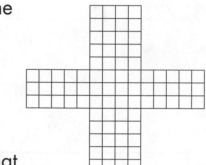

A. 94

C. 60

B. 82

D. 12

3. What is the volume of a rectangular prism that
is 4 units by 3 units by 8 units?

A. 15 cubic units

C. 56 cubic units

B. 30 cubic units

D. 96 cubic units

4. Martin has a box with dimensions $3 \times 3 \times 5$.
What are the dimensions of a box that will hold
twice as many cubes as Martin's box?

A. $3 \times 6 \times 5$

C. $6 \times 6 \times 10$

B. $3 \times 6 \times 10$

D. $9 \times 3 \times 5$

5. How many packages like the one shown at the right
will fit in the box shown in Problem 1? Will the box be
completely filled? Explain how you found your answer.

Volume of Boxes

Give the dimensions of each box that can be made
by the pattern shown or by each box pictured.
Then give the number of cubes that will fit.

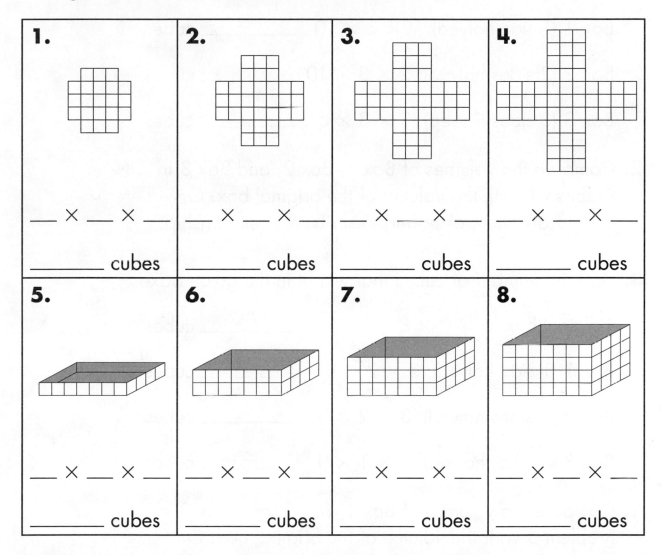

1.

____ × ____ × ____

_____ cubes

2.

____ × ____ × ____

_____ cubes

3.

____ × ____ × ____

_____ cubes

4.

____ × ____ × ____

_____ cubes

5.

____ × ____ × ____

_____ cubes

6.

____ × ____ × ____

_____ cubes

7.

____ × ____ × ____

_____ cubes

8.

____ × ____ × ____

_____ cubes

9. How many cubes will fit in a box that is 6 units
by 9 units on the bottom and 4 units high?

_____ cubes

New Dimensions

1. Find the number of cubes that will fit in the given boxes.

Original box: $4 \times 6 \times 10$ _____ cubes

Box 1 (1 side halved): $4 \times 3 \times 10$ _____ cubes

Box 2 (2 sides halved): $2 \times 3 \times 10$ _____ cubes

Box 3 (3 sides halved): $2 \times 3 \times 5$ _____ cubes

2. Compare the volumes of Box 1, Box 2, and Box 3 in Problem 1 with the volume of the original box. On a separate sheet of paper, describe the relationship.

3. Find the number of cubes that will fit in the given boxes.

Original box: $6 \times 2 \times 8$ _____ cubes

Box 1 (1 side halved): $3 \times 2 \times 8$ _____ cubes

Box 2 (2 sides halved): $3 \times 2 \times 4$ _____ cubes

Box 3 (3 sides halved): $3 \times 1 \times 4$ _____ cubes

4. Compare the volumes of Box 1, Box 2, and Box 3 in Problem 3 with the volume of the original box. On a separate sheet of paper, describe the relationship.

5. Do you think the relationship you describe in Problems 2 and 4 will hold for any box? On a separate sheet of paper, explain why this happens.

 Unit 2

Quiz

Choose the correct answer.

1. Tamira found the volume of her classroom and said it was 230. What unit of measure did she use?

    A. centimeters   **C.** cubic centimeters

    B. square meters   **D.** cubic meters

2. Which is the length of an edge of a cubic meter?

    A. 1 centimeter   **C.** 2 meters

    B. 1 meter   **D.** 3 meters

3. Which is the volume of a rectangular prism with dimensions 3 centimeters by 5 centimeters by 8 centimeters?

    A. 16 cubic centimeters   **C.** 120 cubic centimeters

    B. 40 cubic centimeters   **D.** 240 cubic centimeters

4. Which is the volume of a room that is 8 meters long, 8 meters wide, and 3 meters high?

    A. 384 cubic meters   **C.** 186 cubic meters

    B. 192 cubic meters   **D.** 48 cubic meters

5. What are the dimensions of a box that has half the volume of the box pictured?

4 cm
4 cm
10 cm

Volume in Cubic Centimeters

Picture centimeter cubes along the length, width, and height of each of the 2 boxes shown below. Write the dimensions of the boxes.

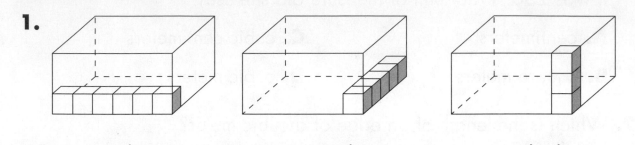

1 cubic centimeter

1.

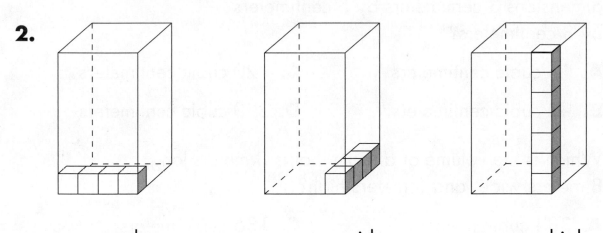

_____ cm long _____ cm wide _____ cm high

What is the volume of this box? Show how you found the answer.

2.

_____ cm long _____ cm wide _____ cm high

What is the volume of this box? Show how you found the answer.

Use anytime after Session 2.1.

Growing Boxes

1. Find the volume of a box with dimensions 3 centimeters by 5 centimeters by 8 centimeters.

_____ cubic centimeters

2. Find the dimensions of a box that has 3 times the volume of the box in Problem 1. Explain how you found your answer.

_____ cm by _____ cm by _____ cm

3. Find the dimensions of a box that has 4 times the volume of the box in Problem 1. Explain how you found your answer.

_____ cm by _____ cm by _____ cm

4. Find the dimensions of a box that has 5 times the volume of the box in Problem 1. Explain how you found your answer.

_____ cm by _____ cm by _____ cm

Quiz

Choose the correct answer.

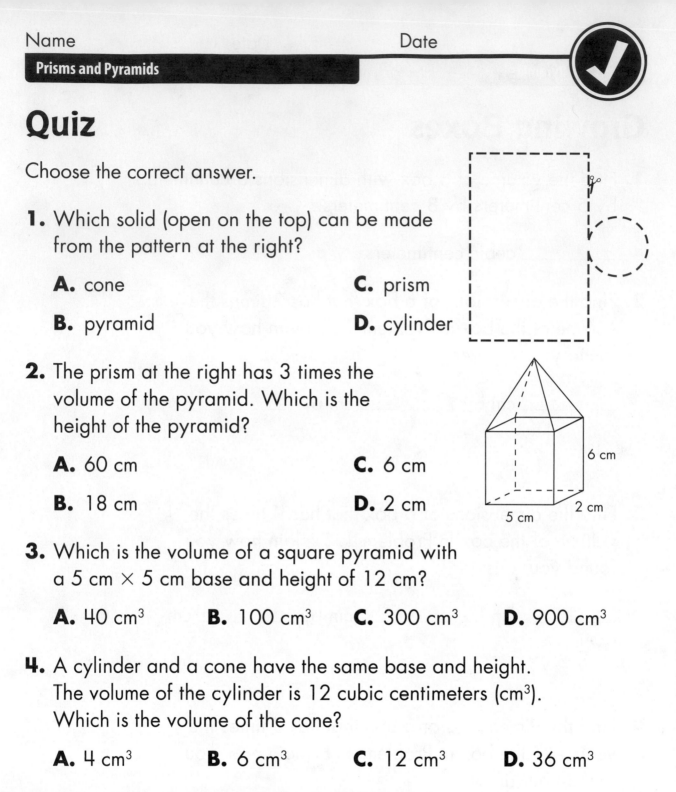

1. Which solid (open on the top) can be made from the pattern at the right?

    A. cone   **C.** prism

    B. pyramid   **D.** cylinder

2. The prism at the right has 3 times the volume of the pyramid. Which is the height of the pyramid?

    A. 60 cm   **C.** 6 cm

    B. 18 cm   **D.** 2 cm

3. Which is the volume of a square pyramid with a 5 cm × 5 cm base and height of 12 cm?

    A. 40 cm³   **B.** 100 cm³   **C.** 300 cm³   **D.** 900 cm³

4. A cylinder and a cone have the same base and height. The volume of the cylinder is 12 cubic centimeters (cm³). Which is the volume of the cone?

    A. 4 cm³   **B.** 6 cm³   **C.** 12 cm³   **D.** 36 cm³

5. A rectangular pyramid has a 3 cm by 4 cm base and a height of 8 cm. Describe a solid that has 3 times the volume of the pyramid.

Using the Three-to-One Relationship

Find the volume of each rectangular prism and
rectangular pyramid.

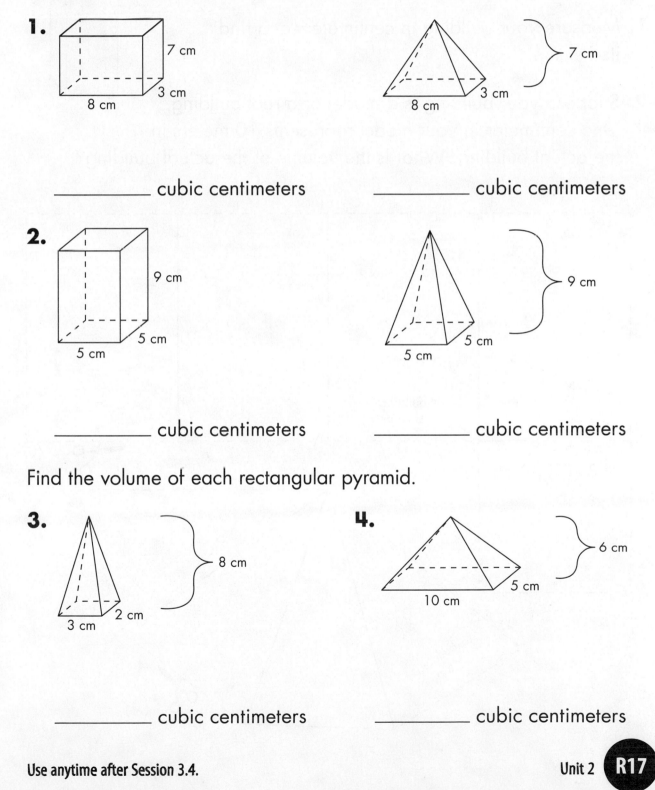

1.

7 cm

3 cm

8 cm

7 cm

3 cm

8 cm

_____ cubic centimeters

_____ cubic centimeters

2.

9 cm

5 cm

5 cm

9 cm

5 cm

5 cm

_____ cubic centimeters

_____ cubic centimeters

Find the volume of each rectangular pyramid.

3.

8 cm

3 cm

2 cm

4.

6 cm

10 cm

5 cm

_____ cubic centimeters

_____ cubic centimeters

Pyramids in Architecture

Cut out the pattern below to make the "building" pictured at the right.

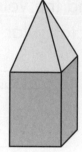

1. Measure your building in centimeters and find its volume.

2. Suppose your building is a model of a real building. One centimeter in your model represents 10 meters in the actual building. What is the volume of the actual building?

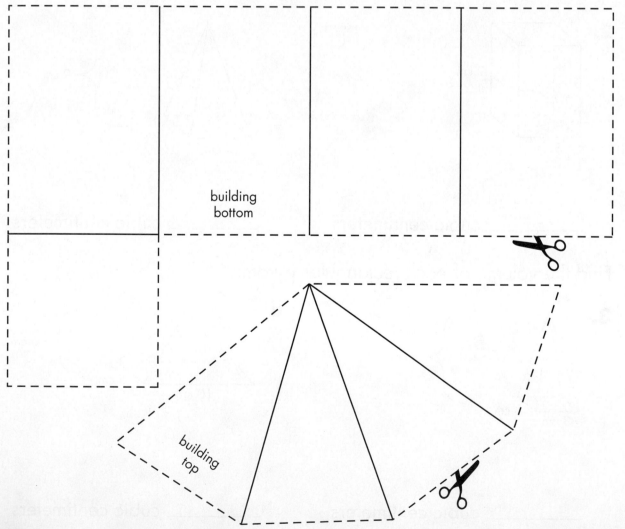

building bottom

building top

Use anytime after Session 3.4.

Quiz

Choose the correct answer.

1. Which shows 100,000 in words?

    A. one thousand

    B. ten thousand

    C. one hundred thousand

    D. one million

2. Start at 4,260. How many steps is it to 10,000?

    A. 14,260   **B.** 6,740   **C.** 5,740   **D.** 1,240

3. Which number is between 27,401 and 27,500?

    A. 27,385   **B.** 26,450   **C.** 27,505   **D.** 27,490

4. 6,211 + 5,000 =

    A. 6,216   **B.** 6,261   **C.** 6,711   **D.** 11,211

5. How can finding 3,649 + 200 help you find 3,649 + 230?

Missing Numbers

Solve each set of problems.

1. $2{,}840 + \underline{\hspace{1.5cm}} = 3{,}000$

$2{,}840 + \underline{\hspace{1.5cm}} = 5{,}000$

$2{,}840 + \underline{\hspace{1.5cm}} = 6{,}000$

$2{,}840 + \underline{\hspace{1.5cm}} = 10{,}000$

2. $4{,}010 + \underline{\hspace{1.5cm}} = 5{,}000$

$4{,}010 + \underline{\hspace{1.5cm}} = 6{,}000$

$4{,}010 + \underline{\hspace{1.5cm}} = 8{,}000$

$4{,}010 + \underline{\hspace{1.5cm}} = 10{,}000$

3. $1{,}375 + \underline{\hspace{1.5cm}} = 2{,}000$

$1{,}375 + \underline{\hspace{1.5cm}} = 5{,}000$

$1{,}375 + \underline{\hspace{1.5cm}} = 7{,}000$

$1{,}375 + \underline{\hspace{1.5cm}} = 10{,}000$

4. $6{,}808 + \underline{\hspace{1.5cm}} = 10{,}000$

5. $3{,}333 + \underline{\hspace{1.5cm}} = 10{,}000$

6. $5{,}519 + \underline{\hspace{1.5cm}} = 10{,}000$

Thousands of Miles, Thousands of Seats

Close to 10,000

Circle the sum that is closer to 10,000.

1. 6,217 + 3,684   6,248 + 3,671

2. 5,506 + 4,125   5,506 + 4,512

3. 1,097 + 8,896   1,967 + 8,089

4. 2,602 + 7,351   6,205 + 3,721

5. 4,008 + 6,119   4,019 + 6,018

6. 3,890 + 6,143   1,343 + 6,609

7. Use the cards below to make two 4-digit numbers with a sum as close as possible to 10,000. Complete the number sentence.

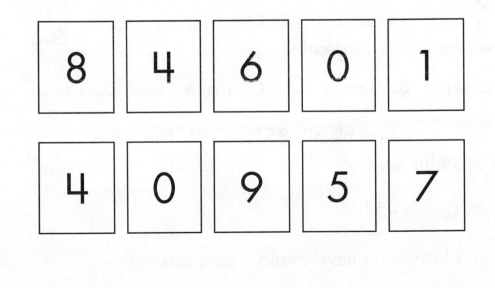

____ ____ ____ ____ + ____ ____ ____ ____ = _____

Quiz

Choose the correct answer.

1. $647 - 271 =$

A. 376   **B.** 366   **C.** 276   **D.** 266

2. Yumiko is driving from Chicago to Phoenix, which is 1,800 miles. She has driven 871 miles. How many miles is she from Phoenix?

A. 929 miles   **C.** 1039 miles

B. 939 miles   **D.** 1071 miles

3. $2,790 - 2,406 =$

A. 284   **B.** 384   **C.** 394   **D.** 396

4. Talisha is using the U.S. algorithm to subtract $734 - 506$.

What does the little 1 represent?

$$\begin{array}{r} 7\overset{2}{\cancel{3}}\overset{1}{4} \\ -\ 506 \\ \hline \end{array}$$

A. 1 hundred   **B.** 4 ones   **C.** 1 one   **D.** 1 ten

5. Joshua is solving the problem $3,851 - 396$. Here is how he began his solution:

$3,851 - 400 = 3,451$

What should Joshua do next? Explain your answer.

Solving Subtraction Problems

Solve the problems below. Show your solutions clearly.

1.
$$735 - 256$$

2.
$$5,716 - 308$$

3.
$$8,264 - 1,138$$

4. Ms. DiFeo has 825 letters to deliver. So far, she has delivered 462 letters. How many letters does she still need to deliver?

5. Mr. Kurinsky is driving 1,410 miles to visit his niece. So far, he has driven 621 miles. How many miles does he still need to drive?

Equivalent Subtraction Problems

Write an equivalent problem for each subtraction problem.
Then find the answer.

1. 833 − 396 = _____

2. 546 − 201 = _____

3. 984 − 149 = _____

4. 628 − 321 = _____

5. 4,037 − 2,010 = _____

6. 7,100 − 2,975 = _____

7. Choose one of the problems above. Explain why the
changes you made resulted in an equivalent problem.

8. Alex is saving for a computer that costs $1,215.
So far he has saved $596. What problem can he
do in his head to figure out how much more money
he needs to buy the computer? Solve the problem.

Use anytime after Session 2.1.

Quiz

Choose the correct answer.

1. Which sum is closest to 7,500?

    A. $2,845 + 4,369$

    B. $6,420 + 984$

    C. $1,999 + 5,603$

    D. $3,905 + 3,730$

2. $14,862 - 10,000 =$

    A. 14,852   **B.** 14,762   **C.** 13,862   **D.** 4,862

3. $49,812 + 12,409 =$

    A. 52,221   **B.** 62,203   **C.** 62,221   **D.** 62,321

4. There are 28,617 students at Central Prairie University. 25,438 students live on the campus. How many students do not live on the campus?

    A. 3,279 students   **C.** 3,189 students

    B. 3,253 students   **D.** 3,179 students

5. Avery is solving $27,705 - 25,680$. He is adding up from 25,680 to 27,705. His first step is shown below. Show how Avery could complete his solution.

$25,680 + 20 = 25,700$

Multistep Problems

1. Granite Mountain Stadium can hold 18,000 people. When the doors opened for a concert, 11,000 people entered the stadium. An hour later, another 5,000 people arrived. How many more people can the stadium hold?

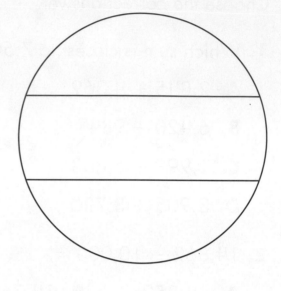

Capacity: _____ people

---

2. The capacity of Prairie Flower Arena is 22,400. At 6:00 P.M., 6,200 people had already arrived for a concert. At 7:00 P.M., another 7,000 people arrived. How many more people can the arena hold?

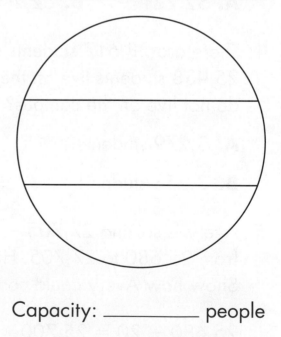

Capacity: _____ people

Use anytime after Session 3.3.

Addition and Subtraction with Large Numbers

Solve the problems below. Show your solutions clearly.

1. 2,410 + 31,500 = _____

2. 51,727 − 14,300 = _____

3. 42,628 + 20,315 = _____

4. 32,860 − 7,085 = _____

5. A stadium has 28,940 seats. 25,256 seats are filled. How many seats are empty?

6. There are 14,602 adults at a concert and 8,099 children. How many people are at the concert?

Quiz

Choose the correct answer.

1. Which does **not** describe the shaded part of the grid?

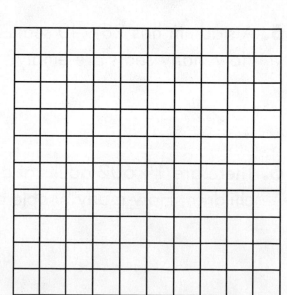

A. $\frac{4}{10}$

B. 4%

C. 40%

D. $\frac{2}{5}$

2. 7% =

A. $\frac{7}{10}$ **B.** $\frac{1}{7}$ **C.** $\frac{7}{100}$ **D.** $\frac{1}{700}$

3. $\frac{5}{8}$ =

A. $12\frac{1}{2}$%   **B.** 58 %   **C.** $62\frac{1}{2}$%   **D.** $66\frac{2}{3}$%

4. On a test of 25 problems, Rachel solved 80% correctly. How many problems did Rachel solve correctly?

A. 20   **B.** 16   **C.** 15   **D.** 8

5. Shade 25% of the grid.

Understanding Fractions and Percents

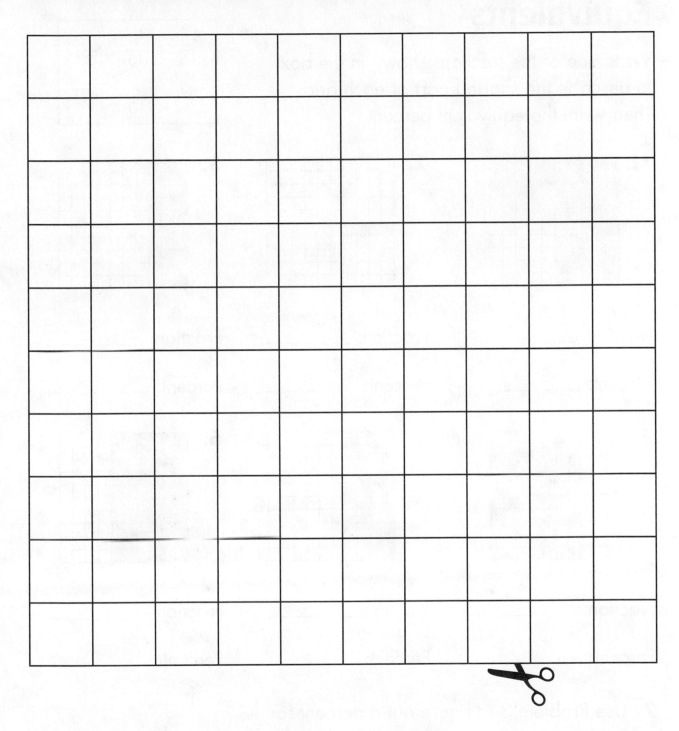

Name _____   Date _____

Finding Fraction and Percent Equivalents

Write one of the fractions shown in the box to describe the shaded part of each grid. Then write the equivalent percent.

$$\frac{3}{5} \quad \frac{1}{10} \quad \frac{1}{3}$$
$$\frac{3}{4} \quad \frac{7}{10} \quad \frac{3}{8}$$

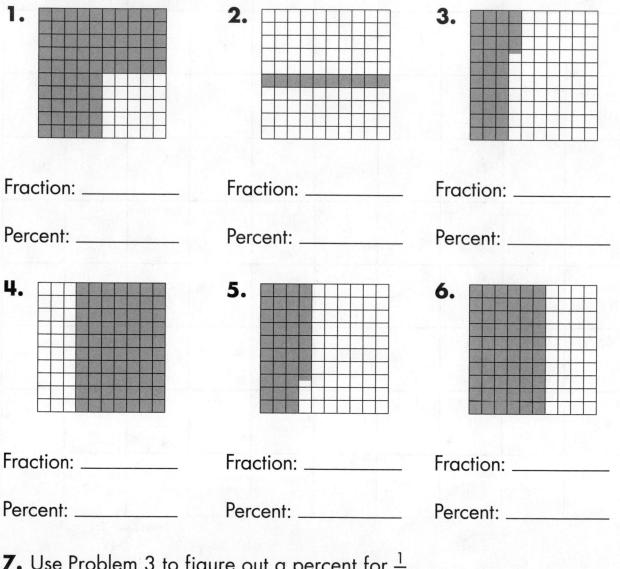

1.

Fraction: _____

Percent: _____

2.

Fraction: _____

Percent: _____

3.

Fraction: _____

Percent: _____

4.

Fraction: _____

Percent: _____

5.

Fraction: _____

Percent: _____

6.

Fraction: _____

Percent: _____

7. Use Problem 3 to figure out a percent for $\frac{1}{6}$. Explain your thinking.

$$\frac{1}{6} = \text{_____}$$

 **R30** Unit 4

Use anytime after Session 1.4.

Quiz

Choose the correct answer.

1. Which is the correct location for $\frac{4}{5}$?

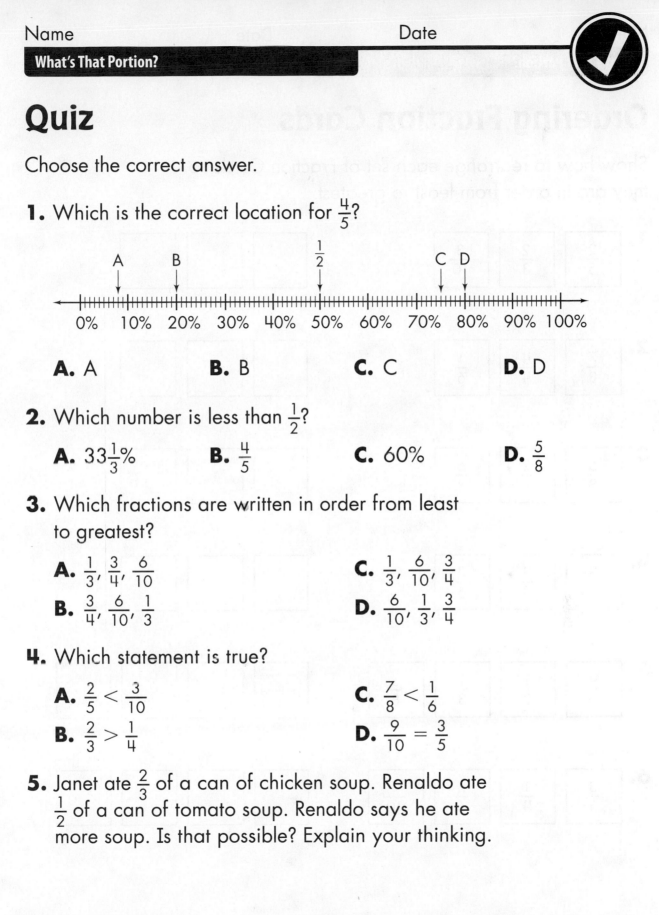

A. A   **B.** B   **C.** C   **D.** D

2. Which number is less than $\frac{1}{2}$?

A. $33\frac{1}{3}\%$ **B.** $\frac{4}{5}$ **C.** 60%   **D.** $\frac{5}{8}$

3. Which fractions are written in order from least to greatest?

A. $\frac{1}{3}, \frac{3}{4}, \frac{6}{10}$ **C.** $\frac{1}{3}, \frac{6}{10}, \frac{3}{4}$

B. $\frac{3}{4}, \frac{6}{10}, \frac{1}{3}$ **D.** $\frac{6}{10}, \frac{1}{3}, \frac{3}{4}$

4. Which statement is true?

A. $\frac{2}{5} < \frac{3}{10}$ **C.** $\frac{7}{8} < \frac{1}{6}$

B. $\frac{2}{3} > \frac{1}{4}$ **D.** $\frac{9}{10} = \frac{3}{5}$

5. Janet ate $\frac{2}{3}$ of a can of chicken soup. Renaldo ate $\frac{1}{2}$ of a can of tomato soup. Renaldo says he ate more soup. Is that possible? Explain your thinking.

What's That Portion?

Ordering Fraction Cards

Show how to rearrange each set of Fraction Cards so they are in order from least to greatest.

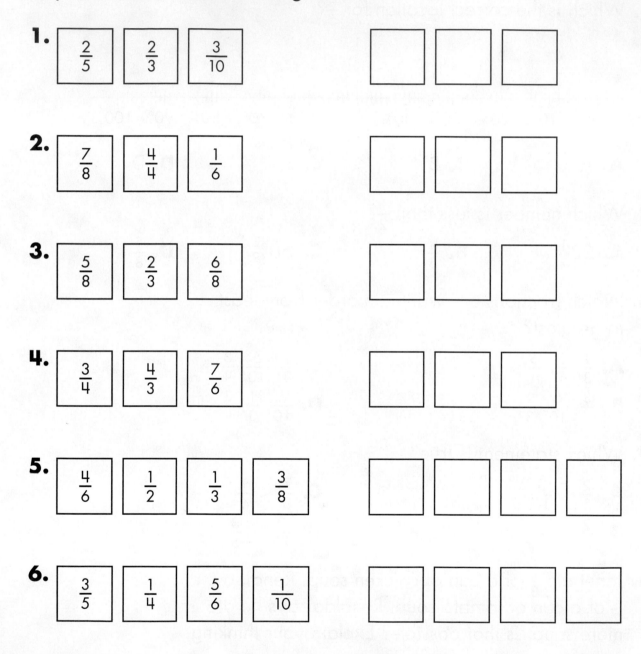

1. $\frac{2}{5}$ $\frac{2}{3}$ $\frac{3}{10}$

2. $\frac{7}{8}$ $\frac{4}{4}$ $\frac{1}{6}$

3. $\frac{5}{8}$ $\frac{2}{3}$ $\frac{6}{8}$

4. $\frac{3}{4}$ $\frac{4}{3}$ $\frac{7}{6}$

5. $\frac{4}{6}$ $\frac{1}{2}$ $\frac{1}{3}$ $\frac{3}{8}$

6. $\frac{3}{5}$ $\frac{1}{4}$ $\frac{5}{6}$ $\frac{1}{10}$

Use anytime after Session 2.3.

Finding Equal Amounts

Solve the problems below. Explain your thinking clearly.

1. Nora and Hana are tiling two floors in their house. By noon, Nora had laid $\frac{3}{4}$ of her tiles. Hana had laid $\frac{1}{2}$ of her tiles. They laid the same number of tiles. How many tiles might each person have started with?

2. At a party, guests drank $\frac{2}{3}$ of the cranberry punch and $\frac{5}{6}$ of the orange punch. They drank the same amount of each. How many ounces of each punch might there have been at the start of the party?

3. Cecilia and Tavon are reading books. Cecilia has read $\frac{3}{5}$ of her book. Tavon has read $\frac{7}{8}$ of his book. They have read the same number of pages. How many pages might there be in each book?

Quiz

Choose the correct answer.

1. Which numbers are written in order from least to greatest?

   A. $1\frac{1}{2}$, $1\frac{7}{8}$, $1\frac{1}{4}$ **C.** $1\frac{7}{8}$, $1\frac{1}{2}$, $1\frac{1}{4}$

   B. $1\frac{1}{4}$, $1\frac{1}{2}$, $1\frac{7}{8}$ **D.** $1\frac{1}{2}$, $1\frac{1}{4}$, $1\frac{7}{8}$

2. Which sum is greater than 1?

   A. $\frac{1}{4} + \frac{1}{3}$ **C.** $\frac{1}{2} + \frac{1}{6}$

   B. $\frac{5}{8} + \frac{1}{4}$ **D.** $\frac{7}{10} + \frac{2}{5}$

3. $\frac{5}{12} + \frac{1}{4} + \frac{1}{2} =$

   A. $1\frac{1}{3}$ **B.** $1\frac{1}{6}$ **C.** $\frac{7}{12}$ **D.** $\frac{7}{18}$

4. $\frac{9}{10} - \frac{2}{5} =$

   A. $\frac{1}{2}$ **B.** $\frac{7}{10}$ **C.** $1\frac{3}{10}$ **D.** $\frac{7}{5}$

5. Describe how to use a clock face to add $\frac{1}{6} + \frac{2}{3}$.

Fraction Addition

Find each sum. Then circle the sum that is closer to 1.
In the space to the right of each problem, write how
you decided which sum is closer to 1.

1. $\frac{1}{4} + \frac{7}{12} =$ _____

    $\frac{2}{3} + \frac{1}{12} =$ _____

2. $\frac{3}{4} + \frac{2}{3} =$ _____

    $\frac{7}{12} + \frac{1}{2} =$ _____

3. $\frac{1}{2} + \frac{3}{4} =$ _____

    $\frac{5}{6} + \frac{1}{12} =$ _____

4. Alicia bought $\frac{1}{6}$ yard of blue
ribbon and $\frac{2}{3}$ yard of purple
ribbon. Walter bought $\frac{1}{2}$ yard
of red ribbon and $\frac{5}{12}$ yard of
green ribbon. Who bought a
total amount of ribbon closer
to 1 yard? _____

Adding Mixed Numbers

Find each sum. Show your work.

1. $1\frac{1}{2} + 1\frac{1}{4} =$ _____

2. $2\frac{1}{3} + 1\frac{3}{4} =$ _____

3. $2\frac{5}{6} + 2\frac{2}{3} =$ _____

4. $3\frac{5}{12} + 2\frac{1}{2} =$ _____

Quiz

Choose the correct answer.

1. Which best describes the triangle?

    A. obtuse triangle   **C.** scalene triangle

    B. acute triangle   **D.** equilateral triangle

2. Which quadrilateral does **not** have 2 pairs of parallel sides?

    A. rectangle   **C.** trapezoid

    B. rhombus   **D.** parallelogram

3. If 3 equal angles are joined to make a right angle, what is the measure of each angle?

    A. 30 degrees   **B.** 45 degrees   **C.** 60 degrees   **D.** 90 degrees

4. Which best describes the polygon at the right?

    A. regular octagon   **C.** quadrilateral

    B. regular hexagon   **D.** decagon

5. Yumiko has 2 paper triangles. She marked an X on 2 angles that are the same size. She put the 2 angles together, and they filled the corner of a sheet of paper. What is the measure of each angle? Explain how you know.

Making Angles

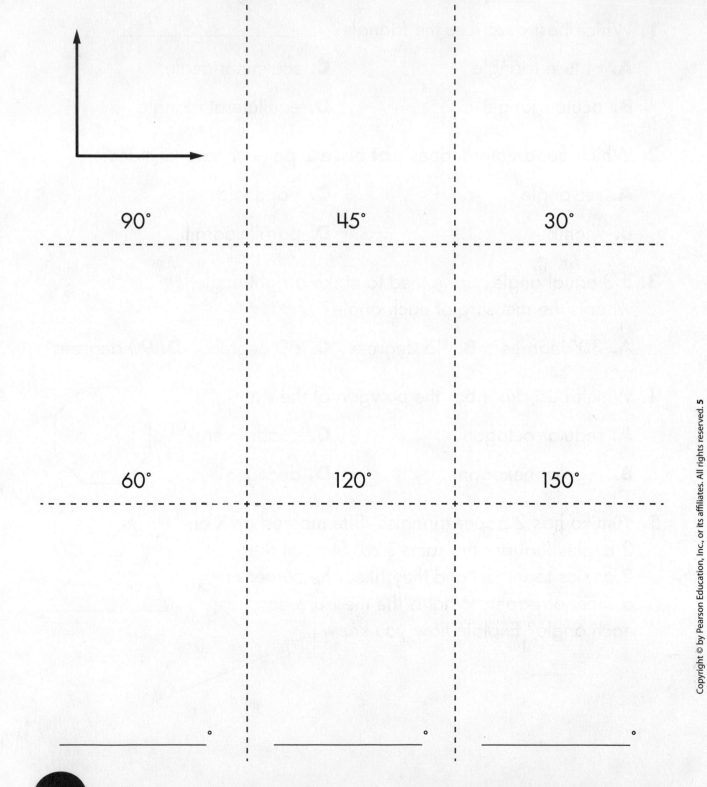

90°

45°

30°

60°

120°

150°

_____ °

_____ °

_____ °

Polygon Puzzles

In each problem, draw at least 1 polygon that fits all the clues.

1. Clue 1: It has 4 sides.
Clue 2: It has at least 1 right angle.
Clue 3: All the sides are the same length.

2. Clue 1: It is a triangle.
Clue 2: It is **not** a regular polygon.
Clue 3: It does not have a right angle.
Clue 4: It has at least 1 acute angle.

3. Clue 1: It is a hexagon.
Clue 2: It is **not** a regular polygon.
Clue 3: It has at least 1 pair of parallel sides.

4. Clue 1: It is a quadrilateral.
Clue 2: It has exactly 1 pair of parallel sides.
Clue 3: It has 2 right angles.

5. Clue 1: It has 4 sides.
Clue 2: It has 2 obtuse angles.
Clue 3: It has 2 acute angles.

6. Clue 1: It is a regular polygon.
Clue 2: All of the angles are acute.

Name _____ Date _____

Quiz

Choose the correct answer.

1. What is the perimeter of this rectangle?

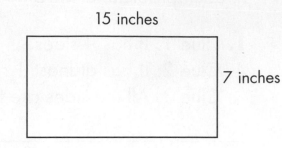

15 inches

7 inches

   A. 105 inches   **C.** 37 inches

   B. 44 inches   **D.** 22 inches

2. What is the area of the rectangle shown in Problem 1?

   A. 22 square inches   **C.** 49 square inches

   B. 44 square inches   **D.** 105 square inches

3. Which are the dimensions of a rectangle that has the same perimeter as the rectangle shown at the right?

4

5

   A. 3 × 6   **C.** 1 × 9

   B. 2 × 10   **D.** 8 × 10

4. Which are the dimensions of a rectangle that has the same area as the rectangle shown in Problem 3?

   A. 8 × 10   **B.** 3 × 6   **C.** 2 × 5   **D.** 2 × 10

5. Martin has 40 feet of fencing to enclose a rectangular garden. Draw 2 different gardens that could be enclosed by the fencing. For each garden, label the dimensions and find the area.

Area and Perimeter Problems

List the dimensions of at least 3 rectangles with the given area or perimeter.

1. area = 32 square inches

2. perimeter = 24 inches

3. area = 48 square inches

4. perimeter = 28 inches

5. Nora's rectangular bedroom rug has an area of 12 square yards. Its perimeter is 14 yards. What are the dimensions of the rug?

6. Benito's garden has an area of 36 square feet. It is surrounded by 24 feet of fencing. What are the dimensions of the garden?

Cutting Up Rectangles

Start with a 24-inch × 10-inch rectangle. Record its perimeter and area in the table. Imagine cutting through the middle of the longer side and rearranging the halves to make a new rectangle. Record the dimensions, perimeter, and area of the new rectangle in the table. Continue splitting the rectangle 5 more times. (Hint: If you are uncertain about how to split a fractional measure in half, look at a ruler.)

Dimensions	Perimeter	Area
1. 24 in. by 10 in.		
2.		
3.		
4.		
5.		
6.		
7.		

8. Look at your completed table. What are some things you notice?

Use anytime after Session 2.4.

Quiz

Choose the correct answer.

1. Which triangle is **not** similar to any of the others?

A.   **B.**   **C.**   **D.**

2. The area of a rectangle is 4 square units. In a similar rectangle, the sides are 3 times as long. Which is the area of the larger polygon?

    A. 12 square units   **C.** 24 square units

    B. 18 square units   **D.** 36 square units

3. Georgia made a trapezoid with 8 triangles. How many triangles would she have to use to make a trapezoid with sides 2 times as long?

    A. 64   **B.** 32   **C.** 16   **D.** 10

4. Which measures are equal in every pair of similar polygons?

    A. side lengths   **C.** angle measures

    B. perimeters   **D.** areas

5. On a sheet of grid paper, draw 2 similar polygons so that one has sides that are 4 times as long as the other. Count squares to find the area of each.

Measuring Polygons

Drawing Similar Shapes

1. On the grid, draw a shape with an area of 8 square units. Use whole squares only. Then draw 2 shapes similar to the original shape. One should have sides that are twice as long as the original shape. The other should have sides that are 3 times as long as the original shape.

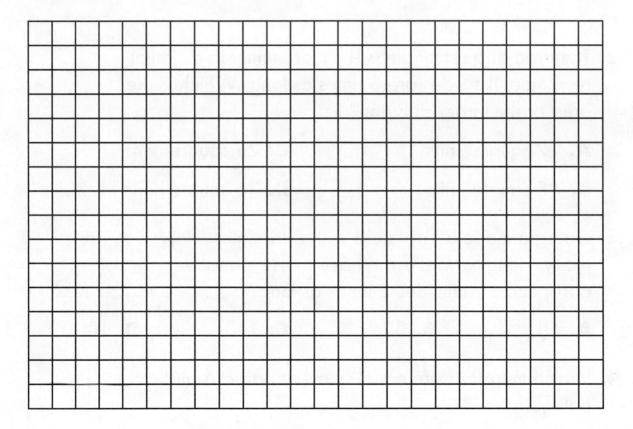

2. Find the area of each shape. Then explain how the areas compare.

Perimeter of Similar Figures

1. Complete the chart.

What is the perimeter of the 10th rectangle?

_____

What is the perimeter of the 25th rectangle?

_____

Rectangle	Perimeter
4 ft × 6 ft	
8 ft × 12 ft	
12 ft × 18 ft	
16 ft × 24 ft	

2. Deon has a 4-inch by 5-inch photo of his dog. He made an enlargement that has sides that are twice as long. He also made a poster that has sides that are 6 times as long. What is the perimeter of each picture?

Original photo: _____

Enlargement: _____

Poster: _____

3. Yumiko drew a plan for a new house. In the plan, the perimeter of the first floor is 3 feet. The first floor of the actual house will have sides that are 60 times as long. Find the perimeter of the first floor of the actual house.

_____

4. A pennant has sides 3 times the sides of the pennant shown at the right. What is the perimeter of the larger pennant?

_____

$2\frac{1}{2}$ ft

1 ft

$2\frac{1}{2}$ ft

Quiz

Choose the correct answer.

1. Which is the correct location for 1.75?

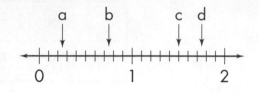

A. a   **B.** b   **C.** c   **D.** d

2. Which number does **not** describe the shaded part of the grid?

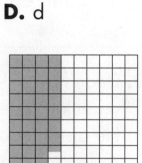

A. 0.375   **C.** 3.75

B. $\frac{375}{1,000}$ **D.** 37.5%

3. In 0.814, what does the 4 represent?

A. 4 ones   **C.** 4 hundredths

B. 4 thousandths   **D.** 4 tenths

4. Which numbers are shown from least to greatest?

A. 0.29, 0.4, 1.3, 0.06   **C.** 1.3, 0.4, 0.29, 0.06

B. 0.4, 0.06, 1.3, 0.29   **D.** 0.06, 0.29, 0.4, 1.3

5. Describe 2 different methods you can use to find a decimal equivalent to $\frac{1}{4}$.

Decimals on a Number Line

Cecilia and her friends held a grasshopper jumping contest. The chart shows how far each person's grasshopper jumped. Use a letter to mark each distance on the number line. The first distance is done for you.

Grasshopper Jumping Contest	
Contestant	**Distance**
A. Cecilia	0.65 meter
B. Avery	0.3 meter
C. Walter	0.677 meter
D. Terrence	0.25 meter
E. Lourdes	0.5 meter
F. Janet	0.85 meter
G. Stuart	0.615 meter
H. Nora	0.79 meter
I. Felix	0.9 meter

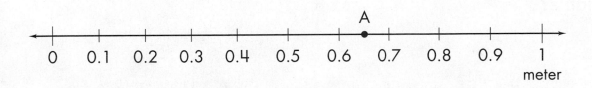

Repeating Decimals

Find the first 3 decimal equivalents. Draw a bar to show which digit or digits repeat. What patterns do you see? Fill out the rest of the table using the pattern, then check your work.

1.

Fraction	Decimal
$\frac{1}{11}$	
$\frac{2}{11}$	
$\frac{3}{11}$	
$\frac{4}{11}$	
$\frac{5}{11}$	
$\frac{6}{11}$	
$\frac{7}{11}$	
$\frac{8}{11}$	
$\frac{9}{11}$	
$\frac{10}{11}$	

2. What pattern(s) did you notice and use to fill in the remainder of the table?

3. Does the pattern you used for the chart work for $\frac{11}{11}$ and $\frac{12}{11}$? Explain why it does or doesn't work.

Use anytime after Session 1.8.

Quiz

Choose the correct answer.

1. Which number shows the total shaded part of the grids?

    A. 1.85

    B. 1.45

    C. 0.45

    D. 0.145

2. 0.76 + 1.55 =

    A. 2.21   **B.** 2.31   **C.** 23.1   **D.** 231

3. Which sum is the greatest?

    A. 0.25 + 0.9   **C.** 0.075 + 0.55

    B. 0.825 + 0.15   **D.** 0.5 + 0.6

4. Hana bought 1.135 pounds of bananas, 2.8 pounds of apples, and 0.88 pound of grapes. What was the total weight of the fruit?

    A. 4.815 pounds   **C.** 3.715 pounds

    B. 3.815 pounds   **D.** 1.251 pounds

5. Circle 2 or more cards whose sum is 1. Show how you figured it out.

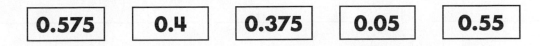

| 0.575 | 0.4 | 0.375 | 0.05 | 0.55 |

Adding Decimals on Grids

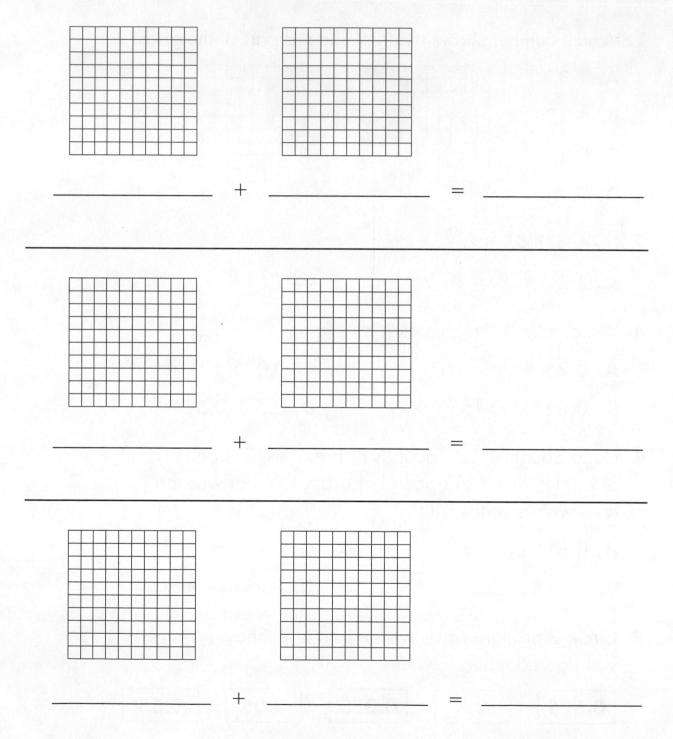

_____ + _____ = _____

_____ + _____ = _____

_____ + _____ = _____

Decimal Addition

Find each sum.

1. 3.2 + 1.9 = _____

2. 2.45 + 2.15 = _____

3. 0.613 + 2.05 = _____

4. 0.9 + 0.15 + 1.3 = _____

5. Find each sum. Then circle the sum that is greater.

6.5 + 1.703 = _____   4.8 + 4.08 = _____

6. Find each sum. Then circle the sum that is closer to 1.

0.505 + 0.4 = _____   0.05 + 0.92 = _____

7. Tyler bought 0.319 pound of Swiss cheese, 0.85 pound of Cheddar cheese, and 1.122 pounds of American cheese. What was the total weight of the cheese?

_____

Quiz

Choose the correct answer.

1. Which equation is illustrated by the diagram?

    A. $4 \times 9 = 9 \times 4$

    B. $4 \times 9 = 12 \times 3$

    C. $12 \times 4 = 8 \times 8$

    D. $12 \times 3 = 6 \times 6$

2. Which is the missing number?

    A. 16   **B.** 8   **C.** 5   **D.** 1

3. Which is **not** equivalent to 18×4?

    A. 3×24 **B.** 6×12 **C.** 9×2 **D.** 9×8

4. Last week, Mitch baked 48 muffins and packaged them in 8 bags with 6 muffins in each bag. This week, he baked twice as many muffins. How many bags does he need if he wants to package them the same way?

    A. 12 bags   **C.** 32 bags

    B. 16 bags   **D.** 96 bags

5. Use a story or a diagram to show why $5 \times 16 = 10 \times 8$.

Equivalent Multiplication Expressions

For each expression, use doubling and halving to write an
equivalent expression.

1. 6×26 _____

2. 8×14 _____

3. 4×50 _____

4. 12×12 _____

For each expression, use tripling and thirding to write
an equivalent expression.

5. 9×24 _____

6. 15×12 _____

7. 36×18 _____

8. 45×24 _____

For each expression, write an equivalent expression.
Try to use a method other than doubling and halving
or tripling and thirding. Describe the method you used.

9. 16×25 _____

10. 12×40 _____

How Many People? How Many Teams?

More Equivalent Multiplication Expressions

Find the missing factors.

1. $5 \times 11 =$ _____ $\times 22$

2. $7 \times 9 = 14 \times$ _____

3. $12 \times 19 = 36 \times$ _____

4. $27 \times 20 =$ _____ $\times 5$

5. Find at least 8 expressions equivalent to 14×33.

6. Pick an expression in Problem 5 that has a fraction or a decimal. Make up a story or draw a representation that illustrates how this expression is equivalent to the original one.

Use anytime after Session 1.3.

Quiz

Choose the correct answer.

1. Georgia multiplied 37 × 53 as shown at the right. What part of the problem does 350 represent?

$$\begin{array}{r} 37 \\ \times\ 53 \\ \hline 21 \\ 90 \\ 350 \\ +\ 1{,}500 \\ \hline 1{,}961 \end{array}$$

A. 30 × 50   **C.** 7 × 5

B. 7 × 50   **D.** 70 × 50

2. Alex multiplied 45 × 28 as shown at the right. What part of the problem does 900 represent?

$$\begin{array}{r} 1 \\ 4 \\ 45 \\ \times\ 28 \\ \hline 360 \\ +\ 900 \\ \hline 1{,}260 \end{array}$$

A. 40 × 20   **C.** 45 × 20

B. 45 × 2   **D.** 45 × 8

3. 68 × 34 =

A. 476   **B.** 2,172   **C.** 2,212   **D.** 2,312

4. A grocer ordered 142 cases of juice. There are 24 cans of juice in each case. How many cans did the grocer order in all?

A. 4,408 cans   **C.** 3,308 cans

B. 3,408 cans   **D.** 852 cans

5. Estimate the product 375 × 22. Show how you made your estimate.

Practicing Multiplication

Solve the problems. Show your work clearly.

1. 32 × 46 = _____

2. 24 × 40 = _____

3. 112 × 37 = _____

4. 19 × 84 = _____

5. 106 × 31 = _____

6. 227 × 53 = _____

Name _____ Date _____

Practicing Multiplication Strategies

Solve each multiplication problem by writing an equivalent problem.

1. $84 \times 15 =$ _____

2. $418 \times 50 =$ _____

Solve each multiplication problem by changing one factor and then making an adjustment.

3. $215 \times 29 =$ _____

4. $121 \times 52 =$ _____

Solve each multiplication problem. Use any strategy.

5. $120 \times 31 =$ _____

6. $888 \times 25 =$ _____

7. $22 \times 35 =$ _____

8. $311 \times 49 =$ _____

Quiz

Choose the correct answer.

1. Which notation can **not** be used to mean how many groups of 16 are in 336?

    A. $16\overline{)336}$ **C.** 16×336

    B. $336 \div 16$ **D.** $\frac{336}{16}$

2. The answer to $514 \div 35$ is

    A. 14 R24   **B.** 14 R14   **C.** 13 R59   **D.** 11 R16

3. The answer to $1{,}200 \div 44$ is

    A. 27 R12   **B.** 27 R22   **C.** 29 R24   **D.** 117 R12

4. A florist has 640 roses. She is making bouquets with 12 roses in each bouquet. How many full bouquets can she make?

    A. 52 bouquets   **C.** 54 bouquets

    B. 53 bouquets   **D.** 63 bouquets

5. Mitch divided 2,650 by 25. His first step is shown below. Show how to complete the problem.

    $2{,}500 \div 25 = 100$

Practicing Division

1. Write the missing numbers.

_____ ÷ 17 = 10

_____ ÷ 17 = 20

_____ ÷ 17 = 30

_____ ÷ 17 = 40

Now, solve this problem:

658 ÷ 17 _____

Solve the following problems.

3. 591 ÷ 13 _____

5. 952 ÷ 31 _____

2. Write the missing numbers.

_____ ÷ 23 = 10

_____ ÷ 23 = 20

_____ ÷ 23 = 30

_____ ÷ 23 = 40

Now, solve this problem:

975 ÷ 23 _____

4. 875 ÷ 35 _____

6. 944 ÷ 22 _____

Practicing Division Strategies

Solve each problem. Do not use the same strategy for
all of the problems.

1. $880 \div 18$ _____

2. $980 \div 28$ _____

3. $1,324 \div 39$ _____

4. $1,632 \div 36$ _____

5. $1,398 \div 76$ _____

6. $2,215 \div 55$ _____

7. Compare 2 different strategies you used. Do you
like one better than the other? Why?

Quiz

Use the chart to choose the correct answer.

Pet Food	Cans per Case	Price per Case
Cat food	36	$55
Dog food	32	$49

1. A pet store placed an order for 504 cans of cat food. How many cases is that?

A. 9 cases   **B.** 10 cases   **C.** 14 cases   **D.** 16 cases

2. A pet hospital ordered 16 cases of dog food. What was the total cost of the dog food?

A. $880   **B.** $816   **C.** $784   **D.** $512

3. Last year, a cat shelter purchased 5 cases of cat food per week. What was the total cost for the year? (Hint: There are 52 weeks in 1 year.)

A. $275   **B.** $1,925   **C.** $12,740   **D.** $14,300

4. A kennel spent $3,300 for cat food and $2,205 for dog food. How many cases of pet food were purchased?

A. 112 cases   **B.** 105 cases   **C.** 100 cases   **D.** 60 cases

5. A dog breeder uses 48 cans of dog food a day. How long will 35 cases of dog food last? Show your work, using clear and concise notation.

Multistep Problems

Solve the problems below. Show your work. Be sure to write your answer clearly.

1. A lawn service mows 18 lawns a day. They are paid $28 for each lawn they mow. How much does the lawn service earn in a 5-day week?

2. Georgia has a bag of 144 beads and two bags with 180 beads in each bag. She uses 28 beads to make a necklace. How many necklaces can she make with the beads she has?

3. Walter had new carpeting installed in his 13-foot by 18-foot family room. They paid $7 per square foot for the carpet and $2 per square foot for the pad under the carpet. What was the total cost for the carpet and pad?

4. A factory made 9,900 bars of soap. They wrapped 6 bars in a package. Then they put 48 packages in a box. How many boxes were completely filled?

Finding the Best Buy

The Service League is putting together gift baskets for the 152 residents of a nursing home. Each basket will contain a jar of jelly, a small loaf of banana bread, and a package of tea bags.

Use the data in the table. Find the least expensive way to purchase the jelly, banana bread, and tea bags. Only full boxes may be purchased. All of the baskets will be the same, so only one type of box for each item will be purchased.

Item	Cost
Jelly	
Box A	$5.50 for 3 jars
Box B	$12.75 for 6 jars
Box C	$18.75 for 10 jars
Banana Bread	
Box D	$9.50 for 4 loaves
Box E	$29.50 for 12 loaves
Tea Bags	
Box F	$14.30 for 5 packages
Box G	$21.42 for 8 packages
Box H	$37.50 for 15 packages

Quiz

Use the graph to choose the correct answer.

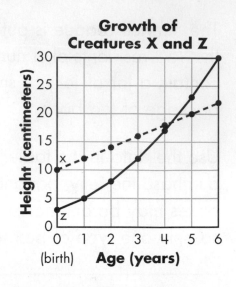

Growth of Creatures X and Z

1. How tall was Creature X at birth?

    A. 2 cm

    B. 3 cm

    C. 10 cm

    D. 22 cm

2. When Creature Z was 12 cm tall, how old was it?

    A. 5 years   **B.** 3 years   **C.** 1 year   **D.** 3 months

3. Which is **not** true about Creature X's and Creature Z's growth?

    A. Creature X's growth was steady.

    B. Creature Z grew a different amount each year.

    C. At birth, Creature X was taller than Creature Z.

    D. Creature Z's growth slowed down as he got older.

4. How much did Creature X grow in 5 years?

    A. 2 cm   **B.** 5 cm   **C.** 10 cm   **D.** 12 cm

5. Did Creature Z's height ever catch up to Creature X's height? How can you tell that from the graph?

Growth Table and Graph

The Quawper is 5 centimeters tall at birth.
It grows 4 centimeters each year.

| Quawper's Growth ||
Age (years)	Height (cm)
0 (birth)	5
1	9
2	13
3	
4	
5	

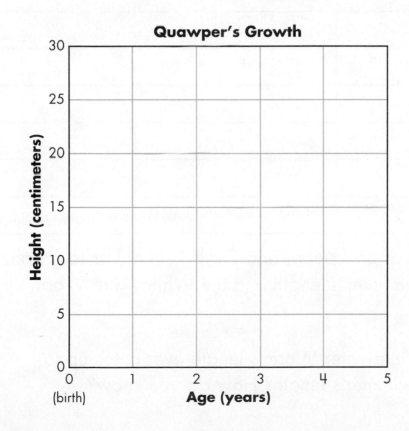

Quawper's Growth

Tables and Graphs

The Slitherswimmer and the Whitewater Worm grow the
same amount each year.

1. Complete the table.

Age (years)	Length (cm)	
	Slitherswimmer	**Whitewater Worm**
0 (birth)	7	3
1	8.5	4.5
2	10	6
3		
4		
5		
6		
7		
8		
9		
10		

2. Use 1 sheet of grid paper and 2 different colors to graph
the Slitherswimmer's length and the Whitewater Worm's
length.

3. Does the Whitewater Worm's length ever catch up to
the Slitherswimmer's length? How do you know?

Use anytime after Session 1.3.

Quiz

Choose the correct answer.

1. Cecilia is making rows of tiles with 8 tiles in each row. What is the rule for finding the total number of tiles in *n* rows?

A. $n + 8$ **B.** $n \times 2$ **C.** $n \times 8$ **D.** $n \times 6$

For Problems 2–5, use the table at the right. The table shows the number of pennies in Felix's and Tavon's Penny Jars.

Round (*n*)	Total Number of Pennies	
	Felix	Tavon
Start with	10	2
1	14	7
2	18	12
3	22	17
4	26	22
5	30	27

2. Felix started with 10 pennies and added 4 pennies in each round. How many pennies will there be in Felix's Penny Jar after 20 rounds?

A. 80 **C.** 200

B. 90 **D.** 204

3. Tavon started with 2 pennies and added 5 pennies in each round. How many pennies will there be in Tavon's Penny Jar after 20 rounds?

A. 127 **B.** 102 **C.** 100 **D.** 45

4. In which round will Tavon's jar catch up to Felix's jar?

A. Round 3 **B.** Round 6 **C.** Round 7 **D.** Round 8

5. Using 1 sheet of grid paper, make a graph for each penny jar. Show both graphs on one grid.

Growth Patterns

Tile Rectangles

Number of Rows	Total Number of Tiles
1	
2	
3	
4	
5	
6	
7	
8	
9	
10	

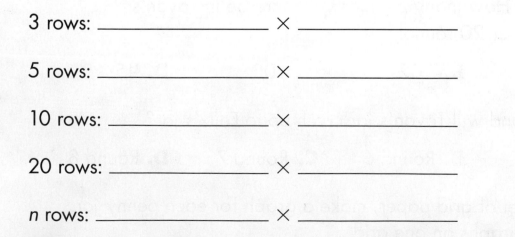

Rules

3 rows: _____ × _____

5 rows: _____ × _____

10 rows: _____ × _____

20 rows: _____ × _____

n rows: _____ × _____

Growth Patterns

Showing Costs In Tables and Graphs

At Jolly Days Amusement Park, a child under 12 pays a
$10 entrance fee and $3 for each ride. A person 12 years
and older pays a $20 entrance fee and $2 for each ride.

1. Complete the table.

2. Use 1 grid and 2 different
colors to graph the costs
shown in the table.
Show the number
of rides along the bottom
of your graph and the
costs along the side.

3. Do the graphs cross each
other? What does that
mean?

Number of Rides	Total Cost	
	Under 12 years old	12 years and older
0 (entrance fee)	$10	$20
1	$13	$22
2	$16	$24
3		
4		
5		
10		
15		
20		

4. The amusement park also
offers an all-day pass that
is good for any number of rides. The pass costs $20.
The customer still has to pay the entrance fee. If you
were going to the park, would you buy the all-day pass?
Explain your thinking.

Quiz

Choose the correct answer.

For Problems 1–5, use the line plots below. They show the number of students in each classroom at 2 schools.

King School: Classroom Sizes (number of students)

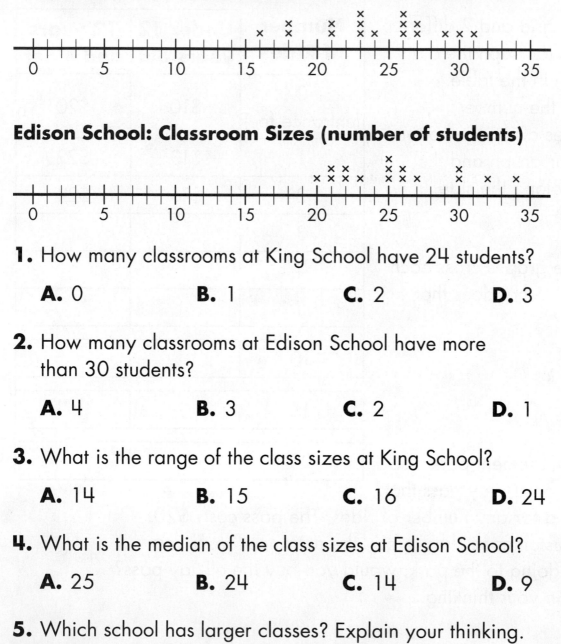

Edison School: Classroom Sizes (number of students)

1. How many classrooms at King School have 24 students?

   A. 0   **B.** 1   **C.** 2   **D.** 3

2. How many classrooms at Edison School have more than 30 students?

   A. 4   **B.** 3   **C.** 2   **D.** 1

3. What is the range of the class sizes at King School?

   A. 14   **B.** 15   **C.** 16   **D.** 24

4. What is the median of the class sizes at Edison School?

   A. 25   **B.** 24   **C.** 14   **D.** 9

5. Which school has larger classes? Explain your thinking.

How Long Can You Stand on One Foot?

Comparing Data

Class Balancing Data

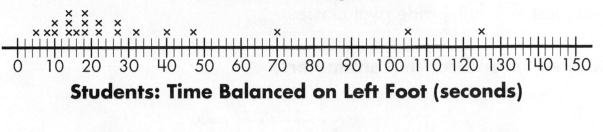

Students: Time Balanced on Left Foot (seconds)

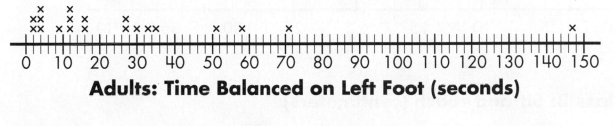

Adults: Time Balanced on Left Foot (seconds)

Ways to describe the data	Students	Adults

Comparing Fitness Tests

These line plots show the results of the sit-and-reach fitness test in 2 fifth-grade gym classes.

Class A: Sit-and-reach (centimeters)

Class B: Sit-and-reach (centimeters)

1. For each class, find the range, median, low score, and high score.

Class A

Range: _____

Median: _____

Low score: _____

High Score: _____

Class B

Range: _____

Median: _____

Low score: _____

High Score: _____

2. Which class had better scores? Explain why you think so.

Use anytime after Session 1.3.

How Long Can You Stand on One Foot?

Quiz

Use the data at the right to choose the correct answer. (Hint: You may want to make your representation for Problem 5 first.)

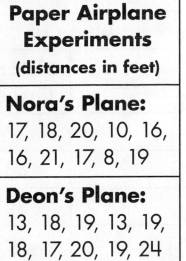

Paper Airplane Experiments
(distances in feet)

Nora's Plane:
17, 18, 20, 10, 16, 16, 21, 17, 8, 19

Deon's Plane:
13, 18, 19, 13, 19, 18, 17, 20, 19, 24

1. What is the median for Nora's data?

    A. 15   **C.** 17

    B. 16   **D.** 18

2. What is the median for Deon's data?

    A. 18.5   **C.** 17.5

    B. 18   **D.** 17

3. Which of the following is greater for Nora's plane than for Deon's plane?

    A. highest value   **C.** range

    B. lowest value   **D.** median

4. Which of the following may **not** be useful when comparing Deon's and Nora's data?

    A. mode   **C.** median

    B. outliers   **D.** range

5. On a separate sheet of paper, make a representation of these sets of data. Write 3 statements comparing the 2 sets of data.

How Long Can You Stand on One Foot?

Line Plots for Two Sets of Data

Blue Car	
Trial	Distance (inches)
1	27
2	38
3	34
4	30
5	28
6	29
7	18
8	20
9	34
10	33

Orange Car	
Trial	Distance (inches)
1	37
2	31
3	30
4	39
5	38
6	21
7	37
8	29
9	36
10	38

0
_____

0
_____

Comparing Data

The students in 2 classes were tested on right-angle push-ups. The results are shown in the line plots.

Room 204: Right-Angle Push-Ups

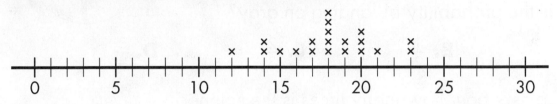

Room 109: Right-Angle Push-Ups

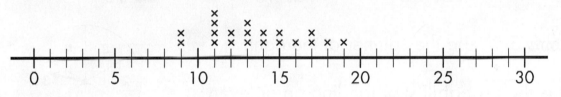

Complete the chart. For Problem 3, make your own choice about what to compare.

What are you comparing?	Room 204	Room 109	Who is better?
1. Median			
2. Highest value			
3.			

4. Who is better at right-angle push-ups? Why?

5. Why might the results be different for the 2 classes?

Quiz

Choose the correct answer.

For Problems 1–2, use the spinner at the right.

1. What is the probability of landing on gray?

   A. $\frac{1}{4}$ **B.** $\frac{1}{2}$ **C.** $\frac{2}{3}$ **D.** $\frac{3}{4}$

2. In 60 spins, about how many times is the spinner likely to land on gray?

   A. 45   **B.** 30   **C.** 15   **D.** 10

For Problems 3–4, use the spinner at the right.

3. What is the probability of landing on an even number?

   A. $\frac{1}{2}$ **B.** $\frac{2}{3}$ **C.** $\frac{3}{4}$ **D.** $\frac{5}{6}$

4. Player 1 and Player 2 use the spinner to play a game. Player 1 scores 4 points when the spinner lands on an odd number. In order to keep the game fair, how many points should Player 2 score when the spinner lands on an even number?

   A. 8 points   **B.** 4 points   **C.** 2 points   **D.** 1 point

5. Player 1 and Player 2 want to use the spinner at the right to play a game. Write a complete set of rules for a fair game.

What Do You Expect?

1. How many times would you expect the spinner at the right to land on W in 100 spins?

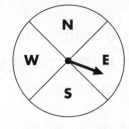

_____

2. How many times would you expect the spinner at the right to land on an even number in 100 spins?

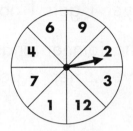

_____

3. Alicia spun a spinner 60 times. She got P 27 times and Q 33 times. Which spinner below do you think she used? Circle your choice. Explain your thinking.

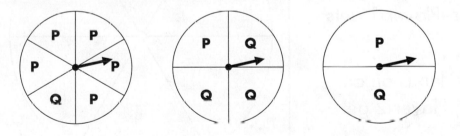

Designing Spinners

1. Design a spinner that can be used in a fair game with the following rules:

- If the spinner lands on X, Player 1 gets 1 point.

- If the spinner lands on Y, Player 2 gets 3 points.

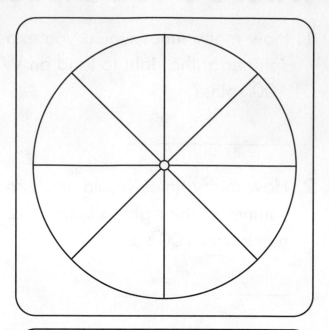

2. Design a spinner that can be used in a fair game with the following rules:

- If the spinner lands on an even number, Player 1 gets 10 points.

- If the spinner lands on an odd number, Player 2 gets 5 points.

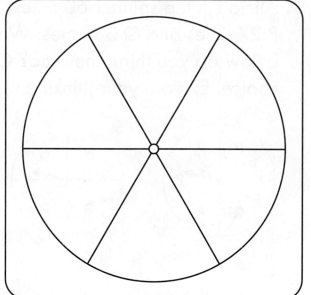

3. Test each of your spinners. Play 20 rounds of each game with another student. (Or play by yourself as both Player 1 and Player 2.) Does it appear that each of your spinners is fair for the game you played?